THE LEAGUE OF
REGRETTABLE SUPERHEROES

Quirk Books
215 Church Street
Philadelphia, PA 19106
quirkbooks.com

THE LEAGUE OF

REGRETTABLE

SUPERHEROES

THE LOOT CRATE EDITION

by JON MORRIS

QUIRK BOOKS

PHILADELPHIA

LRS
★★★★

SUPERHEROES ARE BIG!

Contemporary culture has embraced superheroes in a major way. Hardly a month goes by without an announcement about the release of a new blockbuster superhero movie. Superhero television shows are all over the airwaves, with more waiting in the wings. Superheroes populate our video games, advertising, clothing, and collectibles—even home furnishings. You can make your bed with superhero sheets and light your house with superhero lamps.

Perhaps this ubiquity should come as no surprise. When superheroes burst onto the scene almost eighty years ago, they captured the public imagination like nothing before. Bold, distinctive, and sometimes bizarre, the four-color caped crusaders quickly leapt from drugstore comic book racks to newspapers, radio, movie theaters, and television. True, their popularity has had its ups and downs. But however you look at it, brightly colored defenders of right and goodness like Captain America, Superman, Wonder Woman, and Spider-Man have become household names. Even once-obscure characters like the X-Men or Guardians of the Galaxy have achieved silver screen success.

Still, not every Spandex-clad do-gooder manages to make the big time. From the very origins of the genre to the newest digital graphic novels, the family tree of costumed crimefighters includes hundreds of third-stringers and Z-listers: near-misses, almost-weres, mighta-beens, nice tries, weirdos, oddballs, freaks, and even the occasional innovative idea that was simply ahead of its time.

In the pages that follow, you'll meet largely forgotten heroes, those who walked away from their comic book careers without so much as a participation ribbon to show for it. They are some of the most intriguing also-rans in comics history: super-centaurs, crime-fighting kangaroos, modern-day Draculas, shape-changing spaceships, and even an all-powerful disembodied flying eye. We call these second-tier (or lower) superheroes "regrettable," but it's important to remember that none of these characters are inherently bad. Sometimes, the only factor that kept them from succeeding was bad timing, an unstable marketplace, or merely being lost in the crowd. There's not a single character in this book who doesn't have at least the *potential* to be great. All it takes is the perfect combination of creative team and right audience to make even the wildest idea a wild success.

In fact, several members of the League of Regrettable Superheroes have been revived, revamped, reintroduced, or otherwise regifted with a new lease on life. A few are attempting a comeback even now. In comics, there's always a chance that a seemingly vanished character will come back from extinction. With superheroes becoming more popular with every passing day, you never know when a once-regrettable hero might return and become the next media sensation—or at least find devoted fans among a whole new generation of comics readers.

To count these heroes out and consign them to oblivion without appreciating what they represent—evolving notions of heroism, insights into comics history, and a sampling of fantastic fashion trends in cape-and-cowl ensembles—well, that would be *truly* regrettable.

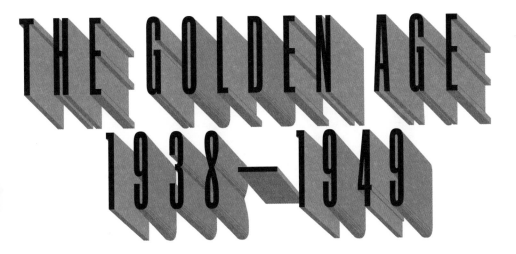

PART ONE

THE GOLDEN AGE 1938–1949

AH, THE GOLDEN AGE OF SUPERHEROES, an exuberant era of two-fisted action and adventure, when every Super-Tom, Wonder-Dick, and Amazing-Harry could throw on a cape and a cowl and give Hitler the business!

Superheroes were a brand-new phenomenon when Superman debuted in *Action Comics* #1, late in the spring of 1938. Prior to the Man of Steel hefting sedans and sending ne'er-do-wells scurrying, colorful crimefighters had been restricted to a few garish characters in the pulp magazines—notably the Spider, the Shadow, and Doc Savage, along with a dozen or so other injustice-intolerant crusaders standing up against evil. These vigilantes possessed elements of superherodom; some had secret identities, some possessed paranormal abilities, some wore what might be considered a costume.

But it was Jerry Siegel and Joe Shuster's red-caped champion who combined those disparate characteristics into a heroic template that is still emulated today. After Superman the floodgates opened, and magazine racks were deluged with atom rays, jet packs, leering villains, and triumphant figures clad in primary-colored costumes leaping over cityscapes. Any word that could precede "-Man" or follow a color suddenly became the sobriquet of a four-color crimebuster. This was a time when the conventions of the superhero genre were still being set, and few ideas seemed too crazy to achieve Superman-level success. Countless publishers scrambled for a foothold in the burgeoning comic book industry, although not all of their efforts met with success. Fortunately for our purposes, the failures tended to be *plenty weird*.

NOTE: Not everyone agrees on the exact limits of these comicbookdom epochs, but the debut of Superman is generally considered the big bang of superhero comics.

711

"I'm #711, and my place is back behind these walls!"

Created by:
George Brenner
(who also created
The Clock—the
first masked hero in
comics!)

Debuted in:
Police Comics #1
(Quality Comics,
August 1941)

Rap sheet:
Perjury, Conspiracy,
Poor Forethought,
Lack of Planning

© 1941 by Quality Comics

SOMETIMES, IT DOESN'T PAY to be a nice guy. Attorney Daniel Dyce finds that out the hard way when he decides to do a favor for his good friend Jacob Horn, whose wife is about to give birth. It seems Horn won't be able to attend the delivery because of a little problem: he's about to begin serving a life sentence behind bars. The scheme the two men hatch is so unlikely that it belongs on the corniest of sitcoms: Dyce will confess to Horn's crimes while Horn visits his wife in the hospital. After a few days, Horn will turn himself in and clear Dyce's name. You'd think an attorney would have devised a better plan . . .

Fate plays its hand and Horn crashes his car en route to the hospital. With his friend dead, no one can clear Dyce, who has no choice but to tunnel out of jail and adopt a crime-fighting identity, of course! Basing his costumed persona on his prison number (and not the famous convenience store), Dyce becomes 711, a caped and masked figure who torments criminals by night and returns to his prison cell by morning. His calling card: a mirrored business card with prison bars painted on it to show criminals their future!

From a crime-fighting perspective, 711's decision to remain in jail pays off in the form of prison gossip, allowing Dyce to eavesdrop on the schemes of his fellow inmates and their nefarious associates. On more than one occasion, the crooks who get busted by 711 end up in the same prison as Dyce. Apparently, this bonus gives the crime-fighter enough satisfaction to keep going back to the Big House.

For the most part, 711 puts the screws to common thugs, crooks, and gangsters. His ultimate enemy is a baddie who repeatedly refers to himself in the third person as "Oscar Jones—Racketeer!" At least one of 711's foes is entertainingly bizarre: Brickbat, a bat-masked figure in a lime-green suit who kills by throwing exploding bricks (packed with deadly gas) at his victims.

The reason 711 hasn't been seen since his first series may be his ignoble method of cancellation: he was fatally shot during a fight with Oscar Jones (racketeer!). To add insult to injury, the only witness to the murder was the hero who would take over 711's feature slot in *Police Comics*, a psychic troubleshooter named Destiny.

THE BLACK DWARF

"That gun in your pocket gives me ideas—bad ideas!"

THE HEAD-SCRATCHING PSEUDONYM of this short-statured superhero seems to imply a mash-up of two distinct schools of exploitation cinema. But whatever drove the Black Dwarf to adopt his outlandish outfit—not to mention his war on crime—remains up to the readers' best guess, for his motives went unexplained. Professional sportsman "Shorty" Wilson, as his nickname implies, stood about shoulder high to the average man. But when this former All-American football star donned his gaucho hat, black robes, and twin automatic pistols, he became the Black Dwarf, scourge of the underworld (his only-slightly-below-average height notwithstanding).

Like the Shadow—whose singular outfit the Black Dwarf's costume seemed to intentionally recall—"Shorty" was aided by a team of agents. His crew consisted of ex-criminals converted to the side of law and order (or at least devoted to ushering crooks to an early grave—the Black Dwarf's gang played rough). They included demolitions expert Nitro, acrobat and stuntman Human Fly (or "Fly," for short), a pickpocket named Dippy, and the Dwarf's girlfriend, the lovely but deadly Arsenic.

Colorful cast aside, the highlight of the Black Dwarf's adventures lay in the language: tough-talking dames and mugs threw around street-level slang with such fluidity that some of the better examples seem almost like poetry. "Ixnay on the horseplay, my noble knave" warns the Dwarf while facing a foe of intimidating stature, "or I'll pop lead pellets into your gizzard!" "You can't play blind man's bluff when your shoes squeak, chum!" he advises on another occasion, before flattening a foe by adding, "Take a bite of knuckle pie!"

When sharp wordplay failed to get results, the Dwarf and his agents were happy to resort to violence. Few other comics of the era would have portrayed the hero cheerily firing a bullet through a bad guy's shooting hand or dangling a ne'er-do-well by a noose around his neck. But the Black Dwarf had no qualms about leaving a trail of dead bodies in his wake.

Circumstances weren't so final for the Black Dwarf, though. When Harry "A" Chesler's line of comics shut down, some of his properties were licensed by publisher St. John and given a second life under new names. With the original art for his adventures relettered and recolored, the Dwarf renewed his war on crime as the Blue Monk, with his girlfriend now donning the more sinister sobriquet "Satana."

Created by:
Paul Gattuso (and Dana Dutch?)

Debuted in:
Spotlight Comics #1 (Harry "A" Chesler Publishing, November 1944)

Also known as:
The Blue Monk, "Hey Shorty!"

THE BOUNCER

"Call me the Bouncer, because I bounced the laziness out of your soul!"

Created by:
Robert Kanigher
and Louis Ferstadt

Debuted in:
The Bouncer,
unnumbered issue
(Fox Features,
1944)

Headquarters:
The Bouncy Castle
(Not really, but
wouldn't that be
great?)

©1944 by Fox Features

EVEN AMONG THE WILD and weird fraternity of absurd superheroes, the Bouncer is a genuine oddball. His superpower: bouncing. His secret identity: a statue. And his sidekick: his own descendant!

The Bouncer is the mythological figure Antaeus (spelled Antaes in the comic), who once wrestled Hercules. This version not only draws strength from the earth, as in the original legend, but also is capable of rebounding from any fall "like a rubber ball." Furthermore, this talent is passed on to his progeny throughout the generations.

Fast-forward to the modern day, when Antaes's latest descendant, Adam Antaes Jr., wants nothing to do with adventure. Still smarting from a controversial career as a collegiate athlete—his semidivine bouncing ability made him a natural at the high jump, and the hurdles were a piece of cake, but his supernatural athleticism also made him the target of detractors and skeptics—Adam decides to retire from physical labor.

Yes, it's the quiet, cerebral life of a sculptor for Adam Jr. But when his friend (and embattled district attorney) John Manly is threatened by a luminous and ruthless criminal named the Glow Worm, adventure comes calling! Without warning, one of Junior's own sculptures of his mythological ancestor comes to life and drags his great-great-great-(etc.)-grandson into battle, the two of them bounding and leaping their way to victory against evil.

The Bouncer and his contemporary partner make for quite a spectacle. Antaes the elder remains decked out in the purple toga and sandals he wore in ancient times, while Antaes Jr. apparently can't be bothered to change out of his work clothes. The apathetic sculptor bounces into action still wearing his plaster-splattered smock and, of course, beret—he is an artist, after all.

Besides bizarre enemies like the Glow Worm and Mr. Lucifer—a circus clown who insists he's the devil—the Bouncer had another interesting gimmick. He invited his readers to join him on his adventures. Youngsters were asked to send in photos and descriptions of themselves (along with parental consent). Two entries were chosen every month to enter the "Comics Hall of Fame" as the Bouncer's guest stars, drawn into the adventures with Antaes Jr. and his high-stepping predecessor. All told, it was an interesting ploy, particularly for a character who already possessed more gimmickry than most.

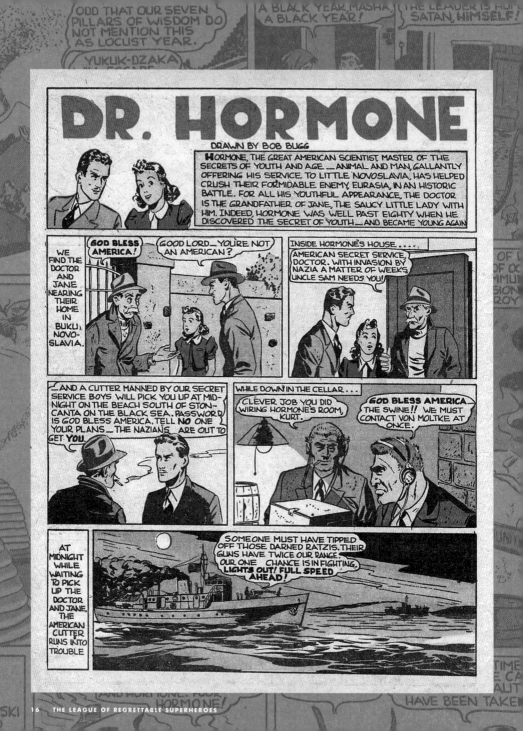

DOCTOR HORMONE

"You want to stop death—I can stop it!
I will increase the size of your army.
I will make your soldiers immune to death!"

THE NAME "DOCTOR HORMONE" may sound like a name you'd see emblazoned on the side of a protein powder concoction or face cream sold on late-night television. He was, in fact, a short-lived superhero who briefly stood against the forces of tyranny in the early 1940s.

An aged scientist who had spent the whole of his life studying the beneficial powers of hormones, Doctor Hormone—evidently his real name, by he way—is rejuvenated upon his deathbed by a "youth hormone" of his own invention, plus a spin under his "angstrom ray machine." Now a fit and energetic young man of twenty-five, the doctor and his granddaughter Janey (that's Janey Hormone, one would assume) bring the mighty power of hormones to benefit the world. Old women are made young again! Babies are grown into men! Boy Scout troops are transformed into full-grown soldiers, and an entire nation is transformed into half-animal human hybrids to repel an invading army! It's actually sort of horrifying as Doctor Hormone plays fast and loose with the lives of children and babies. How many other heroes would be proudly celebrated by a caption describing how he "experiments on a dying infant"?

Another unusual element of Doctor Hormone's brief catalog of adventures is that it was an ongoing serial (most comics at the time featured standalone stories in each issue). During a half dozen adventures, Doctor Hormone pitted the power of his transformative hormone pills first against the evil nation of Eurasia (and its leader Rassinoff, who'd been transformed into a donkey-man and nicknamed "Ass-inoff" by his detractors), and then against an even more insidious foe. Subtly dubbed "Nazia," the aggressive warlike nation was the doctor's persistent enemy through the remainder of his adventures.

Apparently, eternal youth and half-animal soldiers could take Doctor Hormone only so far. In his final appearance, he and his granddaughter are aided in their struggle to keep Texas free of Nazians (and their hooded allies, unmistakably dubbed "The Klan") by a mysterious unseen presence calling itself "The Thinker." A disembodied voice wielding tremendous power, the Thinker grants Doctor Hormone some of his awesome strength. Doc becomes a giant, blows a plane out of the air with super-breath . . . you know, the usual.

At the end of the story, the Thinker brings Dr. Hormone and Janey back through time to his headquarters, a great Roman temple sitting safely amid the hellish whorl of primordial chaos. There, Hormone and Janey sleep, awaiting the Thinker's further orders. They were never heard from again.

Created by:
Robert Bugg

Debuted in:
Popular Comics
#54 (Dell Comics,
August 1940)

Adherence to basic medical ethics:
Spotty

© 1940 by Dell Comics

DOCTOR VAMPIRE

"One murder will not conceal another."

Created by:
Who knows?

Debuted in:
Skyrocket Comics #1
(Harry "A" Chesler
Publishing, ca.
1944)

**Not to be
confused with:**
Librarian
Frankenstein;
Choreographer
Mummy; Wolfman,
Attorney-at-Law

© 1944 Harry "A" Chesler ·
Publishing

EW COMIC CHARACTERS ARE as shrouded in mystery as Doctor Vampire. No credits were included with his sole appearance in Skyrocket Comics (a comic that ran only one issue and was undated), so the identity of his creative team is unknown. Even stranger, the Doctor's singular seven-page adventure leaves a lot to the imagination.

"Shocked by civilization's failure to stamp out the curse that causes the lust to kill," states the character's briefly recounted origin, "Dr. John Rogers deserted his profitable practice to rid humanity of its mad murderers." Fair enough. Armed with a heavy, pointed walking stick, the pseudonymous Doctor Vampire (a doctor of what, exactly?) takes to the night to wipe out the vampire menace.

Whatever his medical specialty, the doctor's pseudonym is a confusing choice. He calls himself Doctor Vampire, but he *fights* vampires. This muddies the water, to say the least. Imagine a Nazi-fighting superhero naming himself Doctor Nazi, a Captain Crime who battled criminals, or the Red Burglar turning out to be a guy who catches burglars.

Doc's one and only adventure takes him to the scene of grisly vampire murders committed at a red barn playhouse (which is in the middle of nowhere yet is depicted as especially popular with the tux-and-tails crowd). As an investigator, Doctor Vamp leaves a lot to be desired. He wanders about the barn, coming face-to-face with a slavering vampire without seeming to recognize his fang-filled mouth for what it is. Maybe they didn't cover this stuff in vampire medical school. Or maybe it wasn't vampires that Doctor Vampire was really hunting. While listening to the band, Doctor Vampire thinks, "Gypsy stuff! Gypsy blood has often been tainted with the killer strain." Whoa, Doctor Vampire, that's racial profiling. Maybe it's for the best that he never made a second appearance.

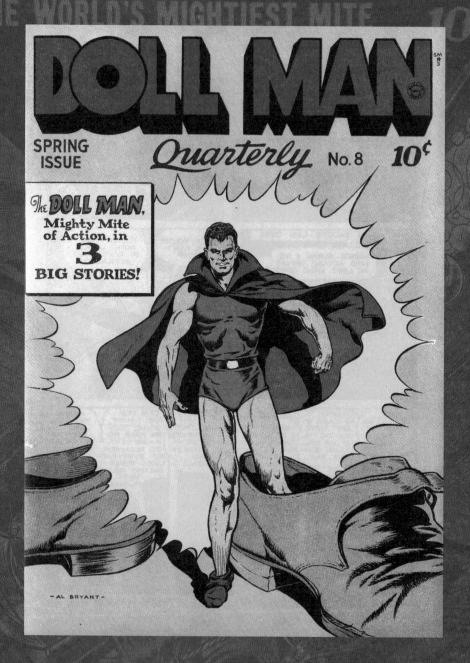

DOLL MAN

"You should know that NO FIST can hold the DOLL MAN!"

F YOU ASK AVERAGE people on the street what superpower they'd like to have, most folks would pick flying, or super-strength, or invisibility—but probably not shrinking. Size reduction is something of a bum super-ability, and even the inch-high heroes for whom getting small is a primary power generally have some extra super-talent to fall back on. Ant-Man, for instance, also controls ants. The Wasp can fire sting-rays. And Shrinking Violet of the Legion of Super-Heroes has Superboy on speed dial.

Darrel "Doll Man" Dane, however, made a career out of shrinking to a modest six inches . . . and that's it. A research chemist who invented a concoction that allowed him to shrink dramatically in stature, he never questioned the limited usefulness of his discovery. His gravitas wasn't helped by his choice of costume: a collared red cape and flimsy sky-blue onesie that left his arms and legs completely bare.

Yet, Doll Man was an immediate hit for its parent publisher, Quality Comics. The so-called World's Mightiest Mite not only regularly nabbed the coveted cover spot on the company's premier anthology title, *Feature Comics*, he soon headlined his own eponymous quarterly book to boot. Despite boasting no other superpower besides standing knee high to a grade-schooler, the daring Doll Man found ways to use his short stature to his advantage: sneaking up on crooks, spying on fifth columnists, and knocking out no-goodniks with a surprisingly full-sized sock on the chin. Typically, Doll Man's adventures hinged on some conveniently fun-sized foe or menace—he found himself fighting trained pets and vicious vermin as often as he tangled with full-sized crooks.

In short order, Doll Man acquired a sidekick—his girlfriend Martha, who shrunk down and adopted the name Doll Girl. Where Darrel had developed his Doll Man powers through chemical means, Martha seemed to have picked up similar shrinking abilities merely by association. Her transformation into Doll Girl was the result of intense concentration and a series of mental exercises designed to replicate Doll Man's six-inch frame. The diminutive duo collected a colorful rogues' gallery, notably the seductive Mademoiselle de Mortire, the cadaverous Corpse, the grotesque Vulture, the leering Skull, and even the Dress Suit, a murderous—but bodiless—set of formal clothes. Doll Man also picked up a pet "Wonder Dog" named Elmo, a Great Dane who often acted as the hero's steed. When transportation by dog wasn't feasible, he hopped onto his "Doll Plane" to get where tiny feet cannot travel.

Created by:
Will Eisner (as "William Erwin Maxwell") and Lou Fine

Debuted in:
Feature Comics #27 (Quality Comics, December 1939)

Vital statistics:
Height: 6 inches; inseam: 3 inches

$\rightarrow$

Reintroduced into comics after a two-decade hiatus—sans girlfriend, dog, and plane—a solo Doll Man was subsequently amped up by his new owners at DC Comics with a mental energy blast meant to even the playing field against average-height adversaries. His increase in powers proved insufficient to renew reader interest in this pint-sized paladin, but Doll Man has enjoyed a few more attempted revivals. Typically, he fights alongside his fellow revived characters from the Quality Comics stable, most recently alongside a new version of the fetching Phantom Lady. But none of these efforts managed to replicate the outsized success of the Doll Man's early career.

ROLL CALL...

Probably twice as many superheroes increase in size compared to those who shrink. They include Giant-Man, Black Goliath, Atlas, Colossal Boy, Apache Chief, Stature, and Tower.

DYNAMITE THOR

"Got a match, buddy?"

Created by:
Wright Lincoln

Debuted in:
Weird Comics #6
(Fox Feature
Syndicate, 1940)

Personality type:
Would it surprise
you if we said
"explosive"?

© Fox Feature Syndicate,
1940

ETER THOR WAS ONE of the world's leading experts on explosives; in fact, he was such a skilled demolitions expert that he'd figured out a way to render himself invulnerable to the devastating power of detonation. Dynamite, nitroglycerin, TNT . . . anything that exploded was just loud noises and puffs of smoke as far as Mr. Thor was concerned. What exactly the guy did to protect his body against blowing up isn't clear. But apparently that's all the impetus he needed to throw on a costume, strap on a belt full of explosives, and launch a crime-fighting career as Dynamite Thor.

For accuracy's sake, it's worth mentioning that although "Dynamite Thor" was the name on the cover, the character's superhero codename was simply "Dynamite" (although he was billed on the cover of his debut issue as "Thor"). Whatever the case, this was the superhero you most hope your child will never emulate, seeing as his powers relied on flinging "explosive pellets" at his foes and whizzing through the air by detonating his dynamite-laden belt.

So, while other flying heroes relied on oversized wings, magic capes, antigravity apparatus, and other nondestructive means of propulsion, Dynamite Thor made himself airborne by detonating the explosives he kept on his belt. One stick of dynamite would launch him skyward; he'd ignite another to change direction, and then fire off a chain of them to travel aerodynamically. It's worth noting that although Dynamite Thor was invulnerable to explosions, bystanders were probably not so lucky. Yes, Dynamite taking flight could be a fatal experience for a crowd of looky-loos.

Explosion-proof Thor was still somehow susceptible to bullets, blackjacks, and a conk on the noggin with a lead pipe. Fortunately, he usually managed to find a way to blow up any immediate threat, and he usually kept a "neutron shield" (whatever that is) handy in case his belt full of explosives didn't do the trick. Less durable was Dynamite Thor's wardrobe—maybe it's all the explosions, but he rarely wore the same outfit twice.

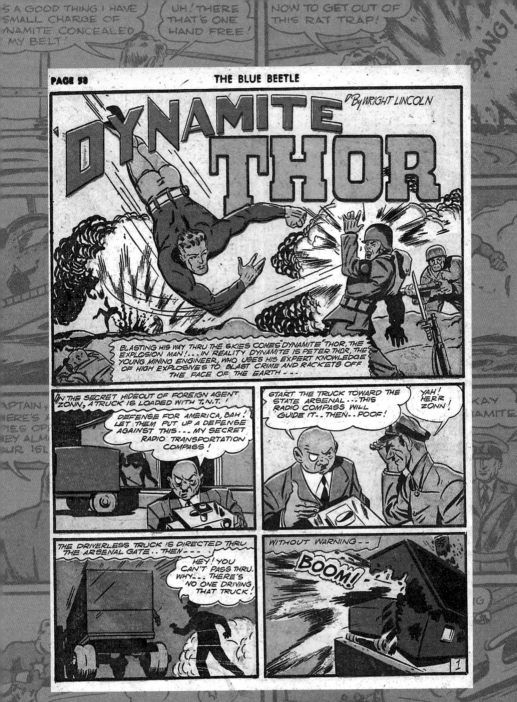

THE EYE

"Fools! To think bullets could harm The Eye!"

OST SUPERHEROIC PSEUDONYMS ARE intended to be understood metaphorically. Iron Man isn't really a man made of iron, Green Lantern isn't a piece of verdant camping equipment, and, by and large, the Beast is in fact a lovely fellow. When it comes to superheroes whose names *can* be taken literally, or, better yet, at—*ahem*—face value, there's no more outstanding example than the Eye.

An actual living, speaking, crime-fighting disembodied floating giant eyeball, the Eye was a mysterious presence that loomed ominously in the pages of *Keen Detective Funnies*, a book that also offered more quotidian fare, such as Dean Denton (Scientific Detective), Dan Dennis F.B.I., and Spark O'Leary, Radio Newshawk.

Appearing amid curtains of flame or billows of smoke, the Eye was in a class by himself (or, uh, itself?). A tireless witness and avenger of injustice, the seemingly supernatural entity possessed an array of powers bordering on the omnipotent. He also seemed to have a few limitations. Despite being able to fly, melt steel, appear and vanish suddenly, manipulate invisible forces, and, oh, be a giant flaming eye all the time, the Eye relied on human assistants to act as his agents against crime.

After appearing in *Keen Detective Funnies* under the masthead of "The Eye Sees!" the Eye went on to star in its own solo book, with an apparent change of career: the ocular avenger was now billed as Detective Eye. Apparently, the Eye had been taking correspondence classes between adventures.

After fewer than a dozen appearances, the Eye vanished as mysteriously as it debuted, and never once had an origin been so much as hinted at. Then again, what kind of origin would explain "The Eye"? Had it once been a man, bitten by a radioactive eye? Was an eye rocketed from a doomed planet, its only survivor? Did an eye burst through a brooding billionaire's library window, inspiring him to fight crime? Perhaps we're better off not knowing.

Created by:
Frank Thomas

Debuted in:
Keen Detective Funnies vol. 2, #12 (Centaur Publications, December 1939)

Also known as:
Detective Eye

© 1939 Centaur Publications

FANTOMAH

"Fantomah wills it!"

Created by:
Fletcher Hanks (as "Barclay Flagg")

Debuted in:
Jungle Comics #2 (Fiction House, February 1940)

Complexion:
Definitely a "Summer," except when she's transformed her head into a blazing skull

© 1940 by Fiction House

HE PRECEDED WONDER WOMAN by more than a year and is arguably the first female superhero in comic books, but chances are you've never heard of Fantomah—Mystery Woman of the Jungle.

Statuesque, white-skinned, blonde-haired, and blue-eyed, at first glance Fantomah appears to share much in common with the other animal-protecting, resource-preserving, leopard-skin-clad "jungle queens" who followed in the footsteps of Sheena, Queen of the Jungle. What makes Fantomah different from her sorority sisters of the savannah, however, has a great deal to do with her creator.

Fletcher Hanks is a legendary and notorious figure in comicdom, having produced the entirety of his strange, alarming, and unpredictable catalog of stories in a brief three-year period before vanishing from the medium. His comics were typified both by bold, stiff, yet informal artwork that recalled woodcut prints and by stories in which near-omnipotent protagonists devised cruel and byzantine punishments for their enemies. Hanks remains one of the most mysterious figures in comics, despite a recently renewed surge of interest in his work (due in large part to a pair of excellent collections edited by Paul Karasik and published by Fantagraphics Books). A reportedly troubled individual, Hanks produced complicated and bizarre creations that seemed to reflect his inner turmoil. In stories that resemble fever dreams, unearthly figures who emerged from mysterious realms and visited elaborate punishments on their enemies were the order of the day.

Like Hanks's other best-remembered creation, Stardust the Super-Wizard, the essentially all-powerful Fantomah was capable of supernatural acts of bizarre chastisement, executed without mercy on plunderers, killers, and would-be tyrants who threatened her domain. She banishes one villain to a dinosaur-populated asteroid, transforms a pair of jewel thieves into creatures resembling a cross between grasshoppers and dandelion leaves, and in one spectacular feat demolishes a squadron of military bomber planes—and all occupants therein—with living sandstorms and a flying formation of jungle lions. Wow!

No less shocking was Fantomah's physical transformation. At rest, she appeared as a gorgeous woman with smoky, mysterious eyes. When angered, however, her skin adopted a sky-blue pallor and her lovely face burned away to reveal a furious blazing skull (although she kept her luxurious golden locks in either state).

$\rightarrow$

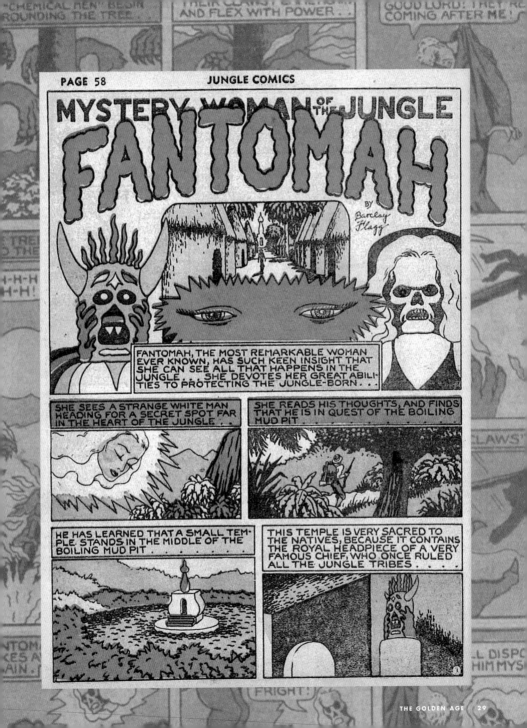

When Hanks left the feature half-way through its run, subsequent writers took the opportunity to tone down the character's extravagances. She was quickly reduced from terrifying omnipotent avenger to the queen of a hidden jungle empire, left to wrestle snakes and panthers with nothing more than her all-too-human cunning and strength, just like all the other girls in the jungle.

ROLL CALL...

Fantomah may have been the first female superhero, but she had plentiful company soon enough, from nonpowered heroines like the Black Cat, Lady Luck, Phantom Lady, and the Woman in Red to superpowered female crime-fighters such as Canadian superheroine Nelvana of the Northern Lights (page 51) and the powerful Miss Victory. Nearly omnipotent superheroines are uncommon in Golden Age comic books, but a few other powerful "goddess" types include Venus, Diana the Huntress, Phara, and the Sorceress of Zoom.

GHOST PATROL

"Funny thing! To know you're ... er ... dead ... an' still be able to talk about it! Well-l-l, we had it comin' ... "

THE GHOST PATROL WEREN'T the only characters in comic books who started their superheroic careers post mortem (see Nemesis, page 95). But few other resurrected super-do-gooders seemed to have as much fun.

In life, the men who would eventually become the Ghost Patrol were lantern-jawed Fred, handsome (and vain) Pedro, and the ironically named Slim. Professional soldiers of fortune, these friends and fellow pilots had the bad timing to enlist in the foreign legion just prior to France falling under Nazi control. Now taking orders from Germany's military commanders stationed in northern Africa, the trio is sent on all manner of unsavory missions, against their better judgment, including a bombing raid targeting helpless civilians.

But their consciences get the better of them in midflight. Underlining their moral quandary, Fred drawls resentfully, "We never joined this outfit to kill women and children!" Deciding to dump their deadly payload harmlessly in the middle of the empty desert, the pilots discover too late that Henri (their mechanic, who had tried to warn them against flying this mission) had sabotaged the planes. Rather than see them used for wholesale slaughter, Henri would see them destroyed by time bombs. An explosive airborne moment later and Fred, Pedro, and Slim have all shuffled off the mortal coil.

But they're not gone long. The reason for the resurrection is never fully explained, but the pilots find themselves standing above their own broken bodies. Even more alarmingly, they can see right through one another!

Near-invisibility isn't the only power the newly dubbed Ghost Patrol picks up. Besides the power of flight, they can also pass through solid objects, stretch and even separate their body parts, turn to smoke, summon storms, and call down lightning. Better still, they can become completely visible and solid. In fact, death doesn't seem to be much more than a minor inconvenience for the men, who are happy to turn their powers to bedeviling Nazi aggressors throughout Europe.

Reuniting with Henri, whom they seem to have forgiven for his deathly shenanigans, the Ghost Patrol's first mission is to direct the full complement of their supernatural powers at their evil former commander. Once the local bad guys are sorted, the spectral soldiers aim higher and closer to Berlin. That's right, they spend their second appearance hassling Hitler! Indeed, the Ghost Patrol frequently makes the top Nazi a special priority throughout their career. A stand-out adventure from early in the run involves the men swiping Hitler's

Created by:
Ted Udall,
Emmanuel Demby,
and Frank Harry

Debuted in:
Flash Comics #29
(DC Comics,
May 1942)

Alternate unused identities:
The Lifeless
Legionnaires,
the Departed
Do-Gooders

© 1942 DC Comics

→

false teeth. "Midout mein teesh I cannot shcream . . . und if I cannot shcream, how can I be der Feuhrer?" cries a gum-toothed Hitler into a full-length mirror.

After World War II wrapped up, the Ghost Patrol eked out another half decade of adventuring, shifting their focus from Axis armies to everyday mobsters. In 1949 the group vanished—for real, this time—and the Ghost Patrol has been AWOL from comics ever since. But the nice thing about a concept like this: you can never fully write off any characters who have already beaten death.

INVISIBLE SCARLET O'NEIL

"I'd better remove my clothes so I can swing freely in the ring."

Created by:
Russell Stamm

Debuted in:
Chicago Times
(June 3, 1940)

No relation to:
Imperceptible
Crimson O'Leary,
Undetectable
Alizarin O'Shea

© 1940 by
Chicago Sun Times

T'S NOT EXACTLY A name that strikes terror into the hearts of criminals. But in the early anything-goes days of superheroes, the rules were still being written, and Invisible Scarlet O'Neil helped write them.

The eponymous Ms. O'Neil missed out on being the first female superhero in comics only because her initial appearance was in newspaper comic strips before she made her comic book debut. (Fantomah, page 28, is generally considered the first.) Many of her few contemporaries, like the Woman in Red and Lady Luck, had little but their wits and fists to rely on. Scarlett may have lacked a superheroic alias or costume, but as her nickname implies, she had the advantage of invisibility.

One in a long line of costumed crime-fighters who gain powers from having an ingenious inventor for a father, Scarlet O'Neil acquired her ability to turn transparent when, as a young girl, she poked a curious finger into a ray beam in her father's laboratory. The result: she could now render herself invisible at will. Whenever our heroine needed to pass unseen, the change was triggered by a discreet application of gentle pressure at a specific spot on her wrist.

Scarlet was the creation of Russell Stamm, a former assistant on Dick Tracy who abandoned the hard-boiled, guns-blazing sensibilities of the popular cop strip that gave him his start. As if presaging the parental concern over comic book violence, Scarlet solved her cases without much in the way of bullets or bloodletting; she got by on wits and her innate kindness. Even promotional material boasted of her relative nonviolence: "Action—without blood and thunder!" read one, and "Adventure—exciting but human! Fantasy—but with a humorous twist!"

Not that O'Neil avoided trouble. Her adventures included challenges any superhero would be proud to face, from raging wildfires to gun-happy crooks, even a little time-traveling. But for all its variety, her career wasn't a long one. As superheroes' popularity began to wane, I.S.O. faded with them, though slowly. In 1950, the "invisible" was dropped from her title, and Scarlet's unusual ability was put on display with increasing rarity. After a few more years as just "Scarlet O'Neil," the strip was renamed after a popular, recently introduced character, "Stainless Steel." A year later, it was canceled altogether.

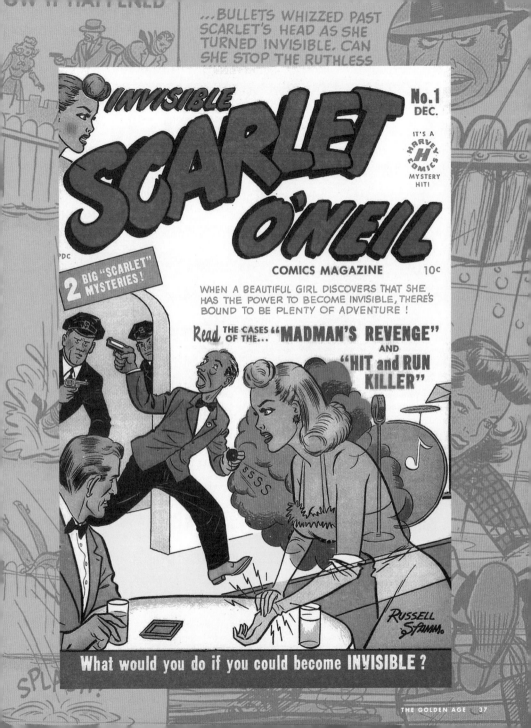

DOLL MAN QUARTERLY

JUST 'N' RIGHT

"Crime robbed me of parental love— something's got to be done to stamp out crime—something will be done!"

T'S AN UNFORTUNATE TRUTH in comic books that many crime-fighting careers begin with the death of one's parents. Superman's mom and dad sacrificed their lives so that their only son might live on. Batman saw his parents gunned down before his very eyes. Even Spider-Man is an orphan. And then . . . there's Just 'n' Right!

On his twenty-sixth birthday, lumberjack Justin Wright is called to the law offices of Cronin, Fox, and Di Preta. There, the burly young man is made aware that he's the sole inheritor of the vast fortune of his late parents—parents he never knew anything about. As an orphan who was handed off from one foster family to another, Justin was also unaware that his parents were murdered by criminals.

Left unsettled by this bittersweet inheritance, Justin goes to explore the humble home left to him. In a small box of mementos he finds his mother's scarf—the same one she was wearing at the time of her murder—and discovers that it possesses a curious one-way translucence. From one side the scarf can be seen through clearly, whereas from the other it's completely opaque. Taking this as a sign, Justin opts to wear the scarf "like a blindfold mask," recalling the likeness of blind justice, as he wages a one-man war on crime.

As aliases go, Justin Wright's baddie-bashing alter ego "Just 'n' Right" probably shouldn't leave crooks scratching their heads about his real name. Nonetheless, he manages to make it work. Decked out in a sharp suit and his mother's scarf, Just 'n' Right is armed with "two rock-like fists as his only weapons," setting upon criminals while "those flying fists flail in the name of justice."

Just 'n' Right enjoys a brief but effective career. In his first outing, he manages to put an end to the nefarious affairs of an elf-eared gangster, Pety Dirk, and top mob boss "Skizone." Part of Just 'n' Right's success may lie in relentless self-promotion. Before we first see him in action, the underworld is already alarmed by "that new menace that's popped up—Just 'n' Right!" Perhaps they'd seen his calling card, a sticker affixed to the foreheads of his unconscious targets depicting a balanced scale and his nom de guerre. The blindfolded baddie-basher doesn't stop at pummeling mooks. To summon the authorities, he hurls a signed note and a bundle of evidence—tied to a brick— through the police chief's office window.

Just 'n' Right made only that single appearance, and his ultimate fate was never revealed. Conceivably, the police picked him up outside the chief's office and put him away on a vandalism charge.

Created by:
George Brenner
(as Wayne Reid)

Debuted in:
Doll Man #1
(Quality Comics, 1941)

Existential dilemma:
Why not become a lumberjack-themed superhero?

LADY SATAN

"Burn, drinker of blood!
Burn, werewolf master!"

Created by:
George Tuska

Debuted in:
Dynamic Comics #1
(Harry "A" Chesler
Publishing,
December 1941)

**Alternate unused
identities:**
Madame
Mephistopheles,
Dame du Devil

ADY SATAN MAY HAVE an infernal edge to her name, but her supernatural side was late in coming. "A strange, mysterious woman dedicates her life to ferret out the secrets of the enemies of democracy," begins the caption to her introductory story, "and to turn these secrets over to the nations engaged in a death struggle to keep the light of liberty aglow."

It's with no light responsibility that Lady Satan has chosen to saddle herself, but she's motivated. The sole survivor of an Atlantic passenger ship sunk by Nazi bombers, the soon-to-be-redubbed Lady Satan (real name unknown) is already vowing revenge while clinging for life to an errant piece of driftwood. She is soon hard at work subverting Nazi war plans, uncovering spies and saboteurs, and generally looking fabulous while doing it—while dining in a chic Parisian café, she's decked out in a blood-red evening dress and matching domino mask.

Lady Satan starts off powerless but not helpless—she's deadly with a garrote, handy with a handgun, and a real pip behind the stick of a fully loaded fighter plane. She relies heavily on her knives, one of which possesses a retractable blade and contains a reservoir for fake blood, in case she needs to simulate a suicide. Her primary weapon, though, is a gun that shoots clouds of chlorine gas. "A dose of chlorine won't hurt them" Lady Satan opines, quite incorrectly, as she fills an entire room of baddies with the deadly stuff.

Lady Satan disappeared for a few years, returning in the mid-1940s after having benefited from a little extracurricular study. Still decked out in her domino mask and crimson eveningwear, Lady Satan picked up some magic tricks—specifically, black magic! Armed with obscure arcana like "Xanda powder" (handy for discouraging overattentive werewolves) and a Tibetan gadget capable of summoning helpful "shadow people," the now-supernatural superheroine finds herself taking on cases of evil mystical forces that threaten innocent people.

A few of her enemies turn out to be merely mortal ne'er-do-wells who use rubber costumes and ghostly gadgets to simulate sorcery. Lady Satan dispatches them just as quickly and mercilessly as she does the legitimate spooks. But she seemed to have given up the chlorine gun, despite its inarguable convenience in dispatching an entire room full of criminal jerks.

MADAM FATAL

"A very touching farewell— clever acting I call it!!"

WHEN ACTOR RICHARD STANTON'S wife passes away and his daughter is kidnapped, the heartbroken but critically acclaimed character actor and master of disguise simply vanishes from public life. Eight years later, Stanton is only a memory. In his place stands Madam Fatal, the little old lady who became comicdom's first cross-dressing superhero!

Resembling something like a mix of the films *Taken* and *Mrs. Doubtfire*, Madam Fatal represents one of the truly unique characters in comics. Women who disguised their gender in superhero identities were uncommon but not unheard of. However, America's macho culture frowned on the opposite arrangement, making Madam Fatal a singular character, to say the least.

Stanton's commitment to his alter ego was more than passing. As explained in his debut appearance, he built a comprehensive second life for his elderly, red-clad senior citizen identity. To Stanton's neighbors, Madam Fatal was a kindly old lady who occupied a quiet apartment with her pet parrot Hamlet, not a superhero vigilante itching for action. Even after Stanton/Fatal confronts his daughter's abductor, he chooses to keep the disguise of Madam Fatal alive. "John Carver is dead," he says of the crook, "and the actor's disguise of Madam Fatal has served its purpose—but this is not enough, for I've decided that, as Madam Fatal, I'll go on fighting crime and lawlessness as long as I can!"

"As long as I can" ended up being another twenty-one issues of *Crack Comics*, during which Madam Fatal never scored a cover appearance (except for a headshot in the sidebar of the first issue, jammed between such timeless names as "Wizard Wells" and "Ned Brant").

Lest readers fear that Stanton was in any way dainty, he was portrayed as an all-around athletic marvel in both of his identities; Stanton was an ex-soldier, a deep-sea diver, and an expert swimmer, whereas Madam Fatal swung from rooftops, fought like a lion, and wielded a ferocious cane. As the series progressed, Carver found himself with more frequent opportunities to appear out of uniform; eventually he was set up in the "Sure-Fire Detective Agency" with his pals Tubby White and Scrappy Nelson (although it was Madam Fatal who did most of the two-fisted sleuthing).

After almost two years, the character had exhausted the shock value inherent in an apparent octogenarian knocking thugs around like rag dolls, and Madam Fatal hung up her wig and cane.

Created by:
Art Pinajian

Debuted in:
Crack Comics #1
(Quality Comics,
May 1940)

Alternate possible aliases:
Old Lady Mortality,
Grandma Death,
that nice Mrs.
Vengeance from
next door

© 1940 by Quality Comics

MOON GIRL

"You have no right to command me in anything!"

Created by:
Max Gaines,
Gardner Fox, and
Sheldon Moldoff

Debuted in:
The Happy Houlihans
#1 (EC Comics,
1947)

Current phase:
Eclipsed

© 1947 by EC Comics

N COMICS, FEMALE SUPERHEROES have always been fewer in number than their male counterparts. But not so few that the creators of superheroines wouldn't copy an already-proven formula.

Moon Girl was the sole costumed hero published by EC Comics, the company that would become notorious for the gory horror comics targeted in Frederic Wertham's excoriating book *Seduction of the Innocent*. Founded by Max Gaines after his departure from All-American Publications (home of Green Lantern, Flash, and, most relevant to Moon Girl, Wonder Woman), Educational Comics was intended to be a comics publisher that eschewed superheroes in favor of religious and didactic stories.

But after Gaines's untimely death in 1947, his son William picked up the reins, steering EC toward the horror, war, and humor comics that became its mainstays. Along the way the company tried its hand at superheroes. Moon Girl's story featured a fairly familiar origin: Clare Lune is princess of an isolated civilization of warrior women. In possession of powers that make her "superior to any man," Clare takes off for America, where, assuming the identity of Moon Girl, she battles evil in her telepathically controlled airship (or, to be more precise, moonship).

Her natural superiority is enhanced by a mystic "moonstone" she wears on a choker. Similarities to Wonder Woman aside, Moon Girl melded adventure with a touch of romance. Part of her mission in America was to locate her former suitor, the rugged Prince Mengu. Finding the dusky hunk teaching school, she adopts a civilian identity in the same institution, pairing up with "The Prince" to fight a parade of primarily female menaces, from the horn-headed Satana to the Invaders from Venus (which apparently, just as the famous self-help book suggested, is where women come from).

Moon Girl had a troubled publishing history. Her comic debuted in the late 1940s, when the shine was already dulling on the superhero craze, and was produced by a publisher for whom costumed adventurers held little interest. When the original title *Moon Girl and the Prince* began to flag in sales, the book was rebranded as simply *Moon Girl*, then the more descriptive *Moon Girl Fights Crime*, then—dropping the superheroic trappings altogether—it was repackaged as a primarily romance comic under the masthead *A Moon, A Girl…Romance!* This last iteration saw a five-issue run, in which Moon Girl eked out only a single appearance.

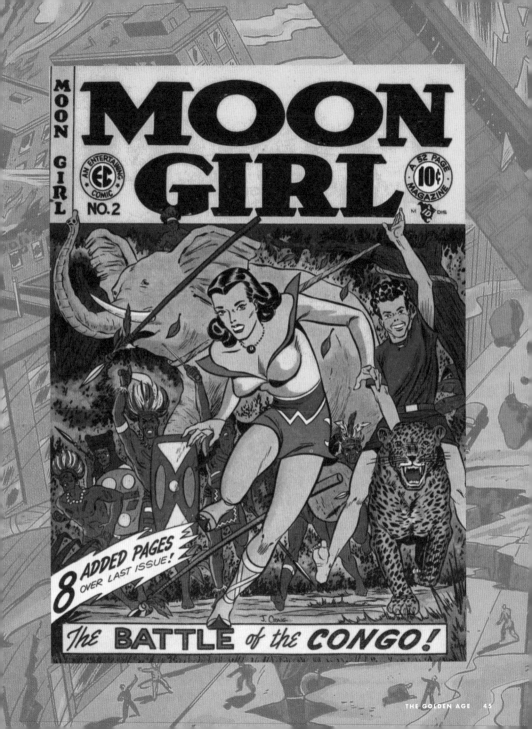

MOTHER HUBBARD

"Loosen eyes from out of head, no more children you'll be fed."

ESPITE BEARING A NAME with origins in a children's nursery rhyme (admittedly, a somewhat bleak one), Mother Hubbard's trio of adventures in the early 1940s may have been the most flat-out terrifying superhero stories in the entire genre. Back then, everyone in a cape and cowl fought a few Nazi masterminds. Only Mother Hubbard confronted a race of gnomes who pried the eyes out of children's heads with a crowbar!

Mother Hubbard was part of a small sorority of magical superheroines (sorcerous do-gooders were not uncommon, but male magicians outnumbered their female counterparts by far), but she stands out from the rest by being a genuine witch—crone-like appearance, peaked hat, flying broomstick, and all. Headquartered in a dilapidated house located somewhere inside a morose swamp, bordering a graveyard and a forest of barren needle-like trees—evidently on the indistinct boundary between the real world and a world of mystical horrors—Mother H turned the tools of witchcraft against the forces of evil, both human and supernatural.

"Remnant of an age long past," begins the caption to her introductory tale, "the mysterious Mother Hubbard commands the power of ancient witchcraft to battle the evils of the present day." Her occult armory was a cupboard that wasn't bare but, rather, full of ominously labeled bottles of "bat's claws," "siren's lure," "madman's blood," and the like. With these, she worked her "idle black magic." She was also in possession of a crystal ball, and Mother Hubbard could tell when evil was afoot via a built-in series of biological early-warning systems. As she once explained, in the rhyming speech that was her trademark patter: "My nose is twitching, my blood runs cold, 'tis sign of pending crime that I must unfold." She could also count on her creaking bones and curling hair to alert her to imminent wrong-doing, although for most folks such bothersome symptoms just mean it's going to rain.

Although she debuted fighting Nazis, Mother Hubbard more often fought bizarre supernatural menaces whose targets were children. In one adventure, work-avoidant gnomes steal the souls of sleeping kiddies and use them to animate tireless wooden dolls to labor on their behalf. In a subsequent adventure, Mother Hubbard blinds a trio of baby-eating ogres and disrupts a subsequent black market for stolen human child's eyes (the gnomes were also responsible for that horrifying operation).

Created by:
Unknown

Debuted in:
Scoop Comics #1
(Harry "A" Chesler
Publishing, 1941)

Sidekick:
Technically,
shouldn't she have
a dog?

→

Our heroine appeared in a few more comics, but those stories were reprinted from her original run in *Scoop*. No new Mother Hubbard stories have popped up since. Maybe she's busy restocking her cupboards.

NELVANA OF THE NORTHERN LIGHTS

"In the name of Koliak, destroy the Etheria!"

COMIC BOOK SUPERHEROES, by and large, began as a uniquely American phenomenon. But it didn't take long for other countries to come up with caped crusaders and dynamic do-gooders all their own. When wartime supply embargoes shut down the shipping of American comic books across the U.S.–Canadian border, Canuck publishers came through with heroes of their own invention and with local flair.

Nelvana wasn't the first superhero to hail from the Great White North. She was preceded by a pair of super-Canucks: the original Iron Man (no relation to Marvel's armored hero) and the seemingly unpowered Freelance. Other Canadian superheroes from the Golden Age of comics include Captain Wonder, Speed Savage, Commander Steel, Sergeant Canuck, and Mr. Monster. But Nelvana was the country's first female superhero, and she even preceded Wonder Woman by several months.

Decked out in a winged headdress and fur-trimmed costume, Nelvana cut an unmistakable figure, dashing through the arctic air and often framed by the aurora borealis. Peculiar to this first class of Canadian superheroes, Nelvana was distinctly tied to the culture and mythology of the land she protected. The demigoddess daughter of "Koliak" and the embodiment of the northern lights, Nelvana, along with her brother Tanero, is charged with protecting the Inuit peoples (whom Nelvana calls "Eskimos," in the parlance of the time) from any and all assorted evils.

Among the abilities shared by Nelvana and her brother are the powers of flight (at light-speed, even), invisibility, telepathy, and weather control. Tanero has his sister beat on one front—he often accompanies her in the form an enormous mastiff-like dog. He exists under a curse that prohibits him from being seen in his human form by "white men." Nelvana suffers no such indignity.

Nelvana has her real-world origins in mythology. Creator Adrian Dingle was inspired by the stories of native Inuit myths told to him by his far-traveling friend Franz Johnston. The result was a popular character whose adventures took her from battling the armies of hidden kingdoms to smashing the Axis to a stint as a secret agent, and finally as Earth's defender against an alien armada. Aside from having to take her brother out for a walk, Nelvana's most regrettable aspect is that she remains largely unknown south of the border. But perhaps her time has come: a small but dedicated legion of fans in her native country are now encouraging the character's revival.

Created by:
Adrian Dingle

Debuted in:
Triumph Adventure Comics #1 (Hillsborough Studio, August 1941)

Favorite bacon:
Canadian

© 1941 by Hillsborough Studio

NIGHTMARE AND SLEEPY
"First you get Sleepy, see?"
"Then you get a Nightmare!"

Created by:
Alan Mandel and
Dan Barry

Debuted in:
Clue Comics
#1 (Hillman
Periodicals,
January 1943)

Day job:
Wrasslin'!

© 1943 by Hillman
Periodicals

OU MIGHT THINK THAT the life of an itinerant professional wrestler would be sufficiently exciting for any individual, traveling from town to town, testing your strength and skill in the squared circle, competing for honors and prizes awarded only to the greatest in the sport. For career grappler Bob White and his teenaged manager Terry Wake, however, wrestling is only the prologue to adventure. Because outside the ring they are, in secret, the outlandish costumed heroes Nightmare and his kid sidekick Sleepy!

Decked out in a garish skeleton costume—which was doused in phosphorescent paint, so as to lend him additional creep factor—the burly Nightmare became a symbol of terror to an assembly of weird and often seemingly supernatural foes, such as the Undertaker, an alleged medieval spirit known as the Robber Baron, and most terrifying of them all, the Corpse That Steals Living Men's Faces!

Despite appearances, neither Nightmare nor his whimsically adorned junior partner Sleepy (decked out in what appears to be footie-pajamas and a red riding hood) boasted any supernatural or superhuman powers. In fact, the duo were all too human; life on the road sometimes left them without money, food, or a place to sleep. Such problems Batman never had!

Halfway through their abbreviated existence, Nightmare and Sleepy lightened the tone. The elder partner dropped his skeleton suit for a more traditional skintight Spandex superhero uniform, complete with encircled "N" insignia on the chest and a pair of "horns" on his cowl (these were more than slightly reminiscent of the "bat-ears" on another grim avenger of the night). Likewise, the light dose of mysticism that shrouded their earlier foes dissipated, leaving Nightmare and Sleepy slugging common thugs, mugs, and the occasional Nazi in lieu of corpse thieves and sundry spirits.

By way of a truly unusual climax to his story, Nightmare's final (and solo) appearance strips the hero of his backstory and reimagines him as a crime-fighting genie summoned by the smoking of a homemade cigar, hand wrapped by slaphappy would-be private detective "Nosey" McGuiness. It's a weird conclusion, but with one last puff, Nightmare and Sleepy were no more.

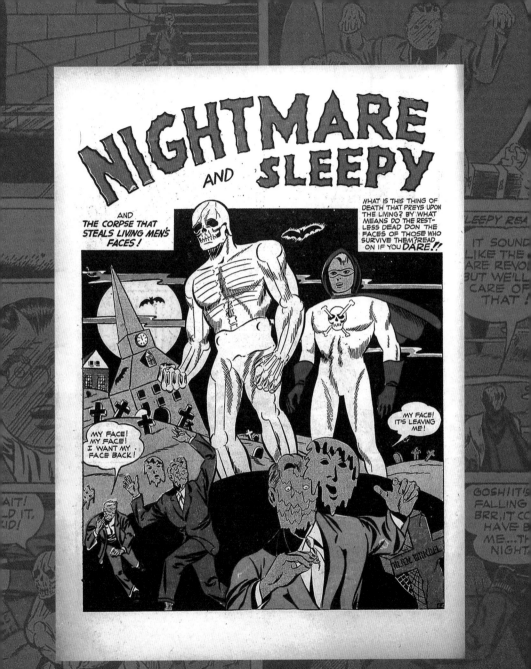

PAT PARKER, WAR NURSE

"We haven't got Cossack horses, but we have got our Yank duck! Let's go!"

OMIC BOOK CRIME-FIGHTERS work in all sorts of courageous careers, from police and private eyes to attorneys and journalists (not to mention the occasional bored wealthy playboys, the bravest heroes of them all). But nursing is a relatively underutilized day job for superheroes—even today, decades after the debut of Pat Parker's costumed identity, War Nurse.

Parker began her comics career as a (lowercase) war nurse, a native London lass whose earliest adventures had her busting up Nazi spy rings when she wasn't providing aid to injured soldiers, all without benefit of a costume or a pseudonym. But when original publisher Brookwood collapsed and Harvey Comics bought the rights to its characters, Nurse Parker received an upgrade to become a fully costumed Axis smasher.

At first so rare as to be nearly nonexistent, female superheroes were soon popping up with increasing regularity after the introduction of Wonder Woman over at Max Gaines's All-American Publishing. Harvey already had a high-profile and popular superheroine in the Black Cat, "Hollywood's Glamorous Detective Star," and the War Nurse would become a secondary lady adventurer. Pat Parker never scored her own series and rarely made cover appearances, whereas the Black Cat was always a popular draw and scored her own series beginning in 1946.

Like her more successful Harvey colleague, Nurse Parker battled crime without the aid of superpowers, relying instead on unexplained fighting skills and an overdose of pluck to see her through. Operating secretly as the mask-wearing War Nurse while holding down a day job as an actual war nurse, Pat maintained possibly the least well-protected double identity in comics history. Perhaps it was her costume that kept people from deducing the truth. Decked out in a midriff-baring boots-and-shorts ensemble—complete with a cowl based on her nurse's hat—her alter ego was certainly an attention getter.

Pat Parker had another crime-fighting career change before her exploits ended. She abandoned her war nurse identity to form the Girl Commandos, a five-girl gang of freedom fighters decked out in identical blue outfits who inserted themselves in the paths of Nazi and imperial Japanese hostilities. Pat stuck with the Girl Commandos until the end of her series, eventually switching out her black hair for blonde and at some point relocating her hometown from London to New York.

The group kept at it for almost two dozen adventures and helped fend off a Japanese invasion of Los Angeles. The onetime War Nurse's shift outlasted the war itself, but not by much—her run officially ended in 1946.

Created by:
Jill Elgin

Debuted in:
Speed Comics #13
(Harvey Comics,
May 1941)

**Not to be
confused with:**
Bob Barker, game
show host; Ma
Barker, gangster

RAINBOW BOY

"Time for Rainbow Boy to see what's cookin'!"

Created by:
Unknown

Debuted in:
*Reg'lar Fellers
Heroic Comics* #14
(Eastern Color
Printing, September
1942)

No relation to:
Rainbow Brite,
Skittles candy

© 1942 by Eastern Color
Printing

THE GOLDEN AGE OF comics had no shortage of heroes sporting the good old red, white, and blue. But one costumed champion beat them all. Sporting the colors of his namesake, it's Rainbow Boy!

As the name suggests, this junior superhero's powers revolved around that colorful arc in the sky, although his origin leaves a lot to the imagination. In his debut appearance, Rainbow Boy explains that he discovered, while experimenting with light while at home, that he could supercharge his body with powerful energy. What sort of experiments isn't clear, but the results couldn't be more bold.

When powered by the sun—or any sufficiently bright light, including flashlights and glowing magma—Rainbow Boy was capable of flying at "the speed of light" while producing a prismatic display in his wake. He could also extend the Roy G. Biv effect at will, using it to form barriers, shields, bridges, even temporary prisons. Though his plain white costume was mostly a blank canvas, his powers more than made up for the monotony with brilliant displays, not to mention the rainbow crest on his helmet.

In his private life, Rainbow Boy was Jay Watson, a boy genius who appears on the Wizard Kid Radio Program, some sort of quiz show for juvenile geniuses. He often teamed up with Eastern's big hitter, the soggy superhero HydroMan, who could turn himself into clear liquid and mentally control bodies of water on command. In fact, Rainbow Boy debuted in HydroMan's feature.

On the few occasions when HydroMan would summon or encounter Rainbow Boy, the pair refused to sit still. With trails of water and rainbows flashing behind them, they would hold impromptu airborne strategy sessions, resembling a dancing-fountains display. (The duo could have made a mint appearing in Las Vegas.)

Rainbow Boy's multihued crusade against crime didn't last long, however. With only nine appearances under his belt, he finally hung up his rainbow-crested hat. There's always a chance he could be revived if the right venue opens up, say, as mascot for a breakfast cereal or greeting card company.

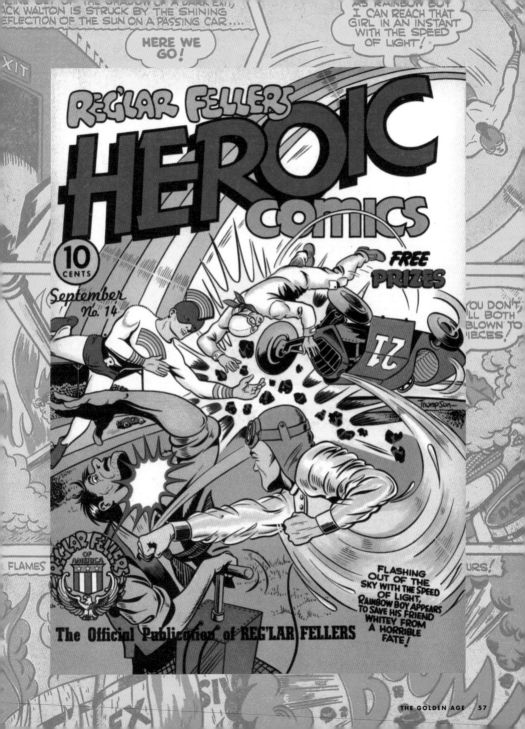

SPEED CENTAUR

"Yes, I've always talked. I'm a talking horse—the only one there is."

ALF THE BATTLE IN coming up with a new superhero is finding a way to make the costumed crime-fighter stand out from the legions of superpowered types competing for a kid's dime (or, these days, four bucks). Well, standing out was no problem for Speed Centaur because he is exactly what his name advertises—a crime-fighting centaur!

Born in a mysterious city somewhere in the Arctic Circle, Speed is the sole survivor of a catastrophic earthquake that destroys his homeland and all of his people. Found orphaned and wandering around by a kindly (human) trapper, the young creature is educated, trained, and raised "to hate evil and crime." On his deathbed, the trapper gives Speed his mission: to clean up the nearby urban center, dubbed "The City of Rackets"!

Well, a trip to the big city is just what every young centaur dreams of, and soon Speed has foiled the plans of his very first crook, "Killer" Diller. For good measure, he's also saved the life of his soon-to-be pal and partner, newsman Jerry "Reel" McCoy.

Speed has an impressive array of powers. As if being a centaur didn't make him unusual enough, he also is a mental and physical giant capable of flinging mighty boulders like pebbles, can apparently fly, and, as his name implies, moves as quickly as lightning. Though he can do much of what other superheroes do, he doesn't have a strong chance for a secret identity, a civilian career, or a romance, despite looking like a matinee idol from the waist up (and also from the waist down, if you count Roy Rogers's horse Trigger).

Speed does have a handy disguise when called on to pass unnoticed in the city: a lifelike equine "mask" with which he covers his upper body, allowing him to pass as a (talking but otherwise unremarkable) urban horse. Disguised in this way, Speed and Reel are able to pass as a street vendor and his innocuous pack animal, thus making Speed the only hero with a nonhuman secret identity.

When not fighting crime, Speed resides in his secret headquarters inside a titanic cave on Nob Nose Mountain, overlooking the city. On the off chance there isn't enough crime and injustice to keep the pair busy in town, the cave is also home to weird monsters. In one its hidden chambers, Speed and Reel face something that resembles a hairy green rhinoceros. They also find the entrance to a lost medieval kingdom, where Speed is able to clean up as the only all-in-one horse-and-rider competitor in jousting history.

Created by:
Martin Kildale

Debuted in:
Amazing Mystery Funnies vol. 2, #8 (Centaur Publications, August 1939)

Weakness:
Well, he likes the occasional sugar cube

© 1939 by Centaur Publications

SPIDER QUEEN

"Ah ah ah, won't you ever learn not to pick on me?"

Created by:
Else Lisau (believed
to be Louis and
Arturo Cazeneuve)

Debuted in:
The Eagle #2
(Fox Features,
September 1941)

Ironic twist:
She still gets
squicked out by
spiders

© 1941 by Fox Features

MASKED RED-AND-BLUE figure appears, using web-shooting wrist devices to swing from the rooftops. An outlaw mistrusted by authorities, the spider-inspired crime-fighter uses scientific powers to defeat evil in its myriad forms. If all that sounds familiar, it should . . . though we're not talking about everyone's favorite neighborhood Spider-Man. This is Spider Queen, a different arachnid-themed do-gooder. Even more significant, she precedes the famous wall crawler by twenty years.

A short-lived superheroine whose few adventures were crammed into the back pages of a comic featuring the patriotic do-gooder known as the Eagle, the woman who would eventually become Spider Queen was research assistant Shannon Kane. After her husband, Harry (a "brilliant young government chemist on a special assignment"), is killed by enemy agents of a foreign government, Shannon discovers his notes for "spider-web fluid." Following the recipe, she creates a thin and durable adhesive that sticks like glue and, as Shannon discovers to her delight, is "actually strong enough to swing on!"

"Ingeniously devising a set of special bracelets to contain the fluid and release it as needed," Shannon effectively invents Spider-Man's trademark web shooters a full two decades before Peter Parker was bitten by his radioactive namesake. Pledging vengeance against the murderers who left her widowed, Shannon declares: "This stuff is going to help me put a damper on some of these gay fellows who make a business out of crime and murder." She then takes to the skyline as Spider Queen.

Like more than a few other costumed crime-fighters in the early days of comics, Spider Queen is considered an outlaw by the local authorities. However, that doesn't stop the hard-hitting police detective Mike O'Bell and the Queen's civilian identity from striking up a flirtatious relationship that runs the length of her three adventures. While hot on the trail of the elusive Spider Queen, Detective O'Bell pays repeated visits to the beautiful young widow. "Gee that's not a bad little doll," he says of Kane, adding, "I like that cute, fluffy type!" He thinks she's not around to hear him . . . but she is. Outside the window, as a matter of fact. Smooth move, O'Bell.

The relentless and cunning Spider Queen was anything but cute and fluffy, but she wasn't particularly long-lived. After three appearances, she vanished from comics, leaving room for the more famous web swinger to take the stage, two decades later.

ZIPPO

"I'll need my full speed to climb this pit ... just like the motorcycles in carnivals!"

TO MAKE YOUR MARK in the highly competitive field of superheroics, you need a gimmick, particularly if your primary power is super-speed. The ability to move at jetlike velocity is such a common characteristic among the cape-and-Spandex set that it's generally appended to a hero's overall abilities. If being fast is your only thing, you'll have to put your own spin on your speed or else become just another Johnny-quick-come-lately.

Which is exactly what private investigator and part-time inventor Joe Blair does when he creates his high-speed alter ego Zippo, "the motor-man on wheels" (according to his own press). Balancing on carborundum wheels and equipped with a below-the-belt exoskeleton outfitted with a powerful compressed-air engine, Zippo turns into a veritable human meteor, traveling at ground speeds of as much as 65 miles an hour. What a rush!

Although he might seem better suited for the extreme-sports circuit, Zippo manages to carve out an impressive eight-issue crime-fighting streak in the pages of *Clue Comics*—practically a lifetime, compared to some other short-lived heroes. It's worth noting, though, that his adventures are always conveniently solved by the clever application of his high-horsepower gizmo. Along with the inevitable high-speed chases, Zippo seems to always find a smooth, flat surface upon which his wheels make of him an exceptional opponent, whether on a high network of steel girders, the side of a massive concrete dam, or even train tracks or telephone wires. And when confined in a space that constrains his movement, Zippo has an additional trick up his pants leg: his durable wheels can whizz fast enough to cut through steel!

Also helping Zippo's batting average is that, defying the usual comic book formula, he never fought foes who claimed super-speed of their own. Typically, he pitted his spinning wheels and pumping pistons against garden-variety crooks and thugs, occasionally turning his attention to the only kind of super-powered foe he tended to fight: weird beast-men. Between the scientist-turned-caveman and would-be world conqueror Professor Schooner, the hulking hairy dwarf called "The Fly," the tubby but catlike "Lynx," and a horrifically ugly "Goblin," Zippo claimed an ugly rogues' gallery that he could literally run rings around.

One character at a time, *Clue Comics* began to cycle out its original lineup of superheroes and replace them with spy, war, and horror features. As if in reverse alphabetical order, the first character shown the door was Zippo. One can imagine the high-speed hero crouched in his signature traveling posture, vanishing into the sunset, unable to outrace his own cancellation.

Created by:
Pierce Rice

Debuted in:
Clue Comics
#1 (Hillman
Publications,
January 1943)

Performance:
40 mpg highway,
28 mpg city

© 1943 by Hillman
Publications

PART TWO

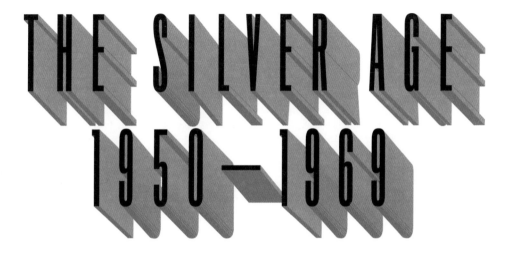

THE SILVER AGE
1950–1969

AFTER THEIR INITIAL WAVE OF SUCCESS IN the 1940s, superheroes began to fall out of favor. An overstuffed marketplace may have been the primary cause. At one point, literally hundreds of costumed do-gooders campaigned for readers' attention (and money) every month. Changing social mores also contributed to the decline, with books like Fredric Wertham's *Seduction of the Innocent* (1954) excoriating comics for an alleged negative influence on children. Even a Senate subcommittee hearing on juvenile delinquency took the material to task. As westerns and space adventures moved in to the public imagination to occupy the spot where caped crusaders once resided, it seemed that superheroes were a fad whose time had come . . . and gone.

But then came the Silver Age! A renewed sense of national optimism—brought about by economic prosperity, leaps in technology, and the drama of the space race—made this a perfect time to bring back the colorful and exciting world of costumed crime-fighters. Inspired by the high-fashion, high-camp spirit of the '60s, superhero comics were infused with a new energy and plenty of strange quirks, aided in no small part by a particular Dynamic Duo's much-celebrated television treatment in 1966. The rise of Marvel Comics changed the way superhero stories were told, injecting the medium with much-needed wit and characterization, and drawing a new audience of high school and college-age readers. As the '60s gaveway to the '70s, it was clear that superheroes were here to stay (even if some of them were too strange to stay in print).

NOTE: By some accounting, the Silver Age of comics started in the mid-1950s, separated from the Golden Age by a few years of artistic stagnation.

BEE-MAN

"We double-dare you to resist the attacking bees!"

Created by:
Otto Binder and
Bill Draut

Debuted in:
*Double-Dare
Adventures* #1
(Harvey Comics,
December 1966)

Headquarters:
The Hive
(a giant hive)

© 1966 by
Harvey Comics

ITH THE ARRIVAL OF Batman to the nation's television screen in 1966, Bat-Mania soon followed. Pop culture went bananas for all sorts of costumed crime-fighters, no matter the flavor. Comics enjoyed a surge of popularity and renewed creativity, and the freshly fertile earth produced literally dozens of over-the-top campy characters. If a premise could be beaten into the ground, comics were there to do it.

Take, for example, Bee-Man. His story begins as disgruntled mission-control technician Barry E. Eames (note the initials) sabotages the landing of a remote-controlled rocket ship, intending to rob the sample-gathering space vessel of whatever wonders it has collected from beyond the surly bonds of earth. Unfortunately, what Eames finds inside the vessel are mutant space bees, which mercilessly savage him and drag his broken body to their distant world.

After an interlude in outer space, Eames returns to earth, decked out in technologically advanced armor from the Bee People's impressive new fall collection of comfortable casualwear for would-be space thieves. The unstoppable Bee-Man occupies himself by stealing gold, radium, and life-giving honey. He stores the loot in his secret, hidden Houston Astrodome–sized beehive headquarters. Surely no one would ever be able to find such a structure, particularly if they were suffering from "Giant Hive Blindness."

Yes, Bee-Man begins his career as a super-crook. By the second issue, however, he's turned himself around, pointing his supersonic wings, honey grenades, and nose-mounted stinger for the cause of justice. Shocked and unsettled by the Bee People's plans to enslave the minds of all humanity (you might even say he was bee-side himself), Bee-Man turns on the Bee Planet's beautiful but cruel "Queen Bea" and aligns himself with the Federal Bureau of Investigation. Officially serving as a superpowered defender of the planet, Bee-Man gains the additional honor of a position as a government operative—yes, he's awarded special-agent status in the one-man "F-Bee-I"!

Bee-Man's career on the side of right was sadly abbreviated. (Or should we say a-bee-viated? No, we probably should not.) After just two appearances, Double-Dare Adventures was canceled and Bee-Man was forced to turn in his wings.

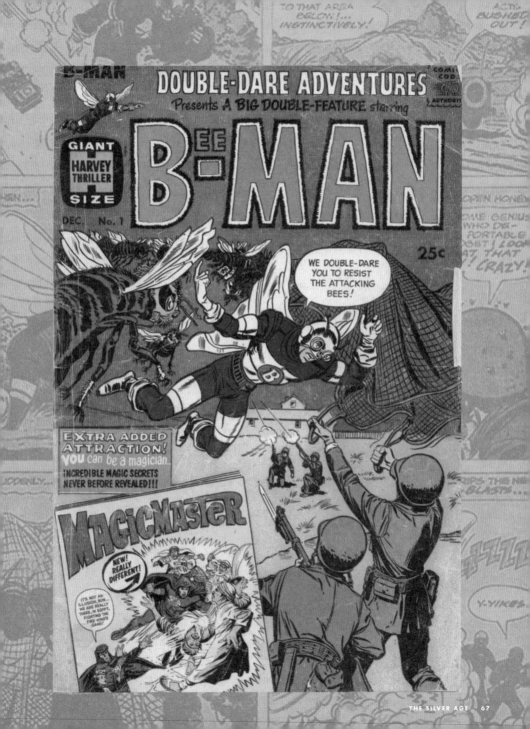

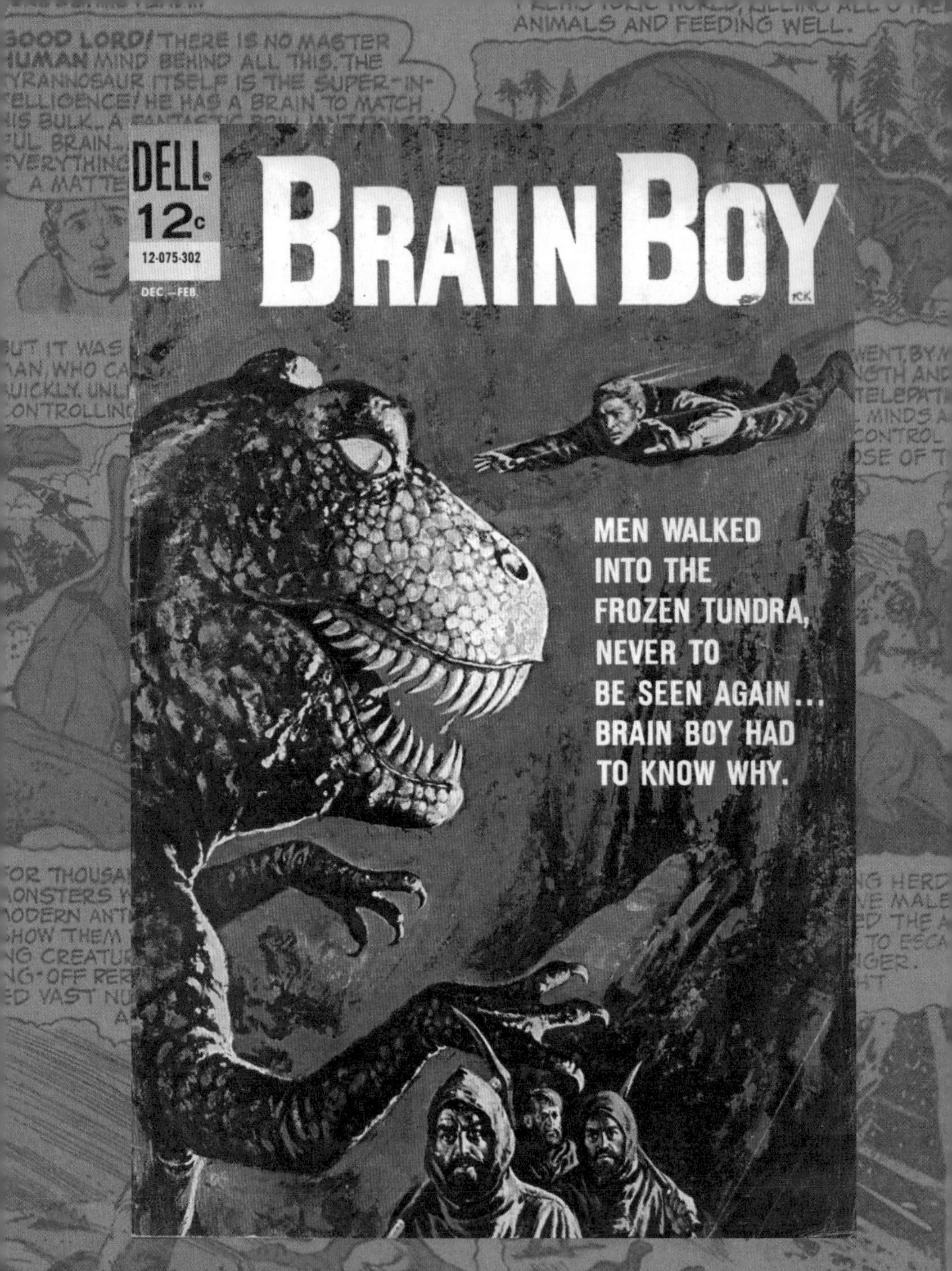
DELL
12c
12-075-302
DEC.—FEB.
BRAIN BOY
MEN WALKED INTO THE FROZEN TUNDRA, NEVER TO BE SEEN AGAIN... BRAIN BOY HAD TO KNOW WHY.

BRAIN BOY

"I'll just take a look into his mind."

SUPERHEROES TEND TO BE a flamboyant lot, what with their colorful sobriquets, dynamic powers, and fanciful costumes. The absence of such trappings may make Brain Boy unique in comics history.

Brain Boy's fate is determined when his parents, Matt Price and his pregnant wife, Mary, collide with an electrical tower after their car loses a tire. Dad perishes in the accident, but mother and fetus survive, and two months later young Matt Junior is born, speaking fluent English! You guessed it: exposure to fatal levels of electrical power has given the future Brain Boy a tremendous intellect and, more than that, the power of "telepathy" (which in this case includes telekinesis, mind control, and a few other fantastic mental abilities).

Matt keeps his telepathic talents a secret, but is nevertheless approached by agents of the American government, who induct him into their service to fight alongside other patriotic telepaths (against, of course, *un*patriotic telepaths). Adopting the nickname "Brain Boy," Matt studies anthropology by day, but by night he's an agent of freedom protecting the West from the Red Menace of Communist ESP!

A product of Dell Comics, Brain Boy was one of the publisher's rare forays into the superhero genre, which could explain his lack of heroic accouterments. Dell produced comics primarily based on the characters of Walt Disney and Warner Bros., as well as dry adaptations of television programs like *Bewitched*, *Maverick*, and *Mission: Impossible*. Brain Boy preceded more colorful Dell super-attempts, like the explosive Nukla and superhero versions of Dracula (page 74) and Frankenstein.

Brain Boy's style was fundamentally more quotidian than these later efforts. He wore normal street clothes during his adventures and answered to his given name more often than his nom de guerre; even his superpowers manifested themselves plainly. There were no force-beams, explosive bolts, flames, or visible psychic shields—he would simply raise a hand to his head or visibly concentrate to flex his telepathic muscles. Despite facing giant dinosaurs and communist armies, the plainclothes Brain Boy lacked the dynamism of your average superhero, which may explain why his initial outing lasted only a half dozen issues.

Created by:
Herb Castle and
Gil Kane

Debuted in:
Four Color Comics
#1330 (Dell Comics,
April/June 1962)

Affiliation:
The Good Ol'
Red, White, and
Telepathic Blue!

© 1962 by Dell Comics

BROTHER POWER THE GEEK

"Man, I tell it like it is now! The sound is groovey! It blows my mind!"

Created by:
Joe Simon

Debuted in:
Brother Power the Geek #1
(DC Comics, October 1968)

Resume:
Tailor's mannequin, student, circus freak, factory-line worker, political candidate, unwilling astronaut

© 1968 by DC Comics

THING THAT LIVES and fights for its soul" is how the enigmatic Brother Power is described on the cover of his debut appearance in late 1968. As leather-clad bikers bear down on his shabby fleeing form, the cover blurbs go on to promise, "Here is the real-life scene of the dangers in Hippie-Land!"

It's unclear how much Joe Simon—who'd cut his teeth on Captain America in the heyday of World War II—truly knew about the realities of hippie culture, aside from what he'd read in the newspaper and seen on TV; by the time he created Brother Power, the comics veteran was fifty-five years old. Still, Simon had a long history of inventing youthful characters. In addition to creating (with partner Jack Kirby) the crime-fighting kid gangs the Newsboy Legion and the Boy Commandoes, he was also the mind behind the pimple-faced protagonists known as the Green Team and the barely shaved chief executive Prez (page 117).

Brother Power's origin is certainly steeped in contemporary touchstones. After a pair of pacifist hippie youths are assaulted by a belligerent biker gang and given a dunk in a nearby river, they dry their clothes on an old tailor's mannequin resting on a radiator. One fortuitous bolt of lightning later and—shades of Frankenstein's monster—the mannequin comes to life and the Geek is born!

Although he hangs out with his hippie pals (and, well, wears their clothes), the creature they dub Brother Power doesn't share their lackadaisical lifestyle. He talks a convincing boho patois, but while his "brothers" are happy to navel-gaze the day away, the Geek has ambition! Before long, Brother Power is hustling up the career ladder and setting his sights on institutional power—Brother Power for Congress! Between job hunting, the Geek uses his surprising strength and fortunate resilience to complicate the schemes of corny criminals, like the wicked bean counter Lord Sliderule.

This troubled title lasted only a pair of issues. Besides suffering from a meandering and genuinely confusing plot, it was rumored that the high-ranking DC Comics editor Mort Weisinger had actively petitioned to kill the hippie-friendly book. Brother Power was unceremoniously fired via rocket into permanent orbit (although he's managed to make a handful of earth-bound appearances in various DC comics since then).

CAPTAIN MARVEL
"SPLIT!" "XAM!"

MORE THAN A FEW superheroes have taken to the skies using the name "Captain Marvel." Most, naturally enough, have been published under the auspices of the Marvel Comics Group, which is intent on preserving its corporate identity in an often crowded marketplace. The original, of course, was the red-suited, lightning-bolt-emblazoned hero whose magic word "Shazam!" echoed in the ears of fans, from comic pages to movie serials to Saturday morning TV.

The Captain Marvel shown here, however, was a short-lived sound-alike from publisher Myron Fass's fly-by-night comics company, eponymously titled M. F. Enterprises. He was crafted by Carl Burgos, whose "Human Torch" creation was one of the three key superheroes published by Timely Comics (primogenitor of Marvel Comics). This new Captain Marvel was something of an amalgam of the two: he bore the first Captain Marvel's name and, like him, was powered by a shouting a magic word. Additionally, like the so-called Human Torch, this Captain Marvel was an android.

Captain Marvel—who was also an alien from another world, just to ensure all bases were covered—possessed possibly the most unique and disturbing superpower in comics history: his limbs fell off. With a cry of "SPLIT!" the good captain's arms, legs, and head would fly free of his torso to tackle a multitude of foes, flip distant switches, or generally create a sense of profound unease. When the individual body parts had achieved their collective goal, the head would holler "XAM!"—not a far cry from the original Captain Marvel's magic word—and the pieces would reunite.

The Captain wasn't the only character in his book to borrow a name from a more popular superhero comic. His kid sidekick was a young fellow named "Billy Baxton" (not dissimilar from the original Cap's secret identity, Billy Batson), and his foes included such familiar super-sobriquets as Plastic Man, Dr. Doom, and Dr. Fate. In fact, his most dreaded enemy was originally called "The Bat," but a cease-and-desist order from DC Comics reminded M. F. Enterprises that it was treading dangerously close to a certain caped crusader. The villain's name was changed to "The Ray" (also the name of a onetime popular superhero).

Ultimately, the troubled Captain M lasted for only a handful of issues. The publisher folded after less than a year, with a measly three titles to its name.

Created by:
Carl Burgos and
Roger Elwood

Debuted in:
Captain Marvel #1
(M. F. Enterprises,
April 1966)

Personal existential dilemma:
If mine eye offend me, should it fly away and fight crime?

© 1966 by M. F. Enterprises

DRACULA

"By changing into my Dracula costume, I will be prepared for anything once I board that lead dirigible."

Created by:
Don Segall and
Tony Tallarico

Debuted in:
Dracula #2; issue #1
was an adaptation
of the film (Dell
Comics, November
1966)

Issue oddity:
Dracula the
superhero appeared
in issues 2–4, then
his adventures were
reprinted in issues
6–8; there was no
Dracula #5

© 1966 by Dell Comics

ELL COMICS ONLY INFREQUENTLY dabbled in original superheroes; their bread and butter was a line of comics licensed from popular television shows, cartoons, and films. So perhaps it's only natural that when they created their own thematically united superhero "universe," they stuck with what worked: repurposing existing characters.

Dracula was part of a trio of superhero titles produced by Dell and based loosely (and therefore legally) on the popular Universal Monsters franchise. The company had already published successful adaptations of several monster movies, including *The Mummy* and *The Creature from the Black Lagoon*. For their line of superheroes, however, Dell went with the classic monster trinity, creating superheroic versions of Dracula, Frankenstein, and Werewolf (the name "Wolf-Man" was legally owned by Universal, so Dell opted for the next best nomenclature). Frankenstein was elevated from rampaging brute to crook-crushing superhero—sort of a cross between Superman, the Hulk, and a morgue full of stitched-together body parts—while the Werewolf became a masked government agent operating in secrecy to save the free world.

As for Dracula, he ended up clothed in a skintight purple bodysuit, with a broad red belt and some sort of bat-eared bonnet. This Dracula was the direct modern-day descendant of the historical King of the Vampires and a research scientist who sets up in the ancestral castle home of his forebears. This contemporary version is seeking a chemical cure for traumatic brain injuries, and the secret ingredient to his sanity-restoring serum is, of course, bat blood.

Accidentally consuming an extra-large dose of his still-untested liquid, in a sort of superheroic equivalent of the old "You got chocolate in my peanut butter" routine, young Doc Dracula is shocked to discover that he has suddenly developed a host of superpowers reminiscent of legendary vampires. He acquires superhuman strength, enhanced senses, and the ability to transform himself into a bat. (Which begs the question: Were the bats he used for his serum transformed vampires, caught in a moment of vulnerability?)

Abandoning his research, young Dracula devotes his newfound powers to the cause of clearing the ol' family name, which has been tainted by the atrocities of his famous ancestor (why can no one ever recall all the *good* things the Draculas have done?). Designing a costume and setting off for America, the newly rechristened Dracula makes this oath:

> *"I pledge by the strange powers which have become mine to fight against the injustice, corruption, evil and greed which fills this Earth in the hopes that* →

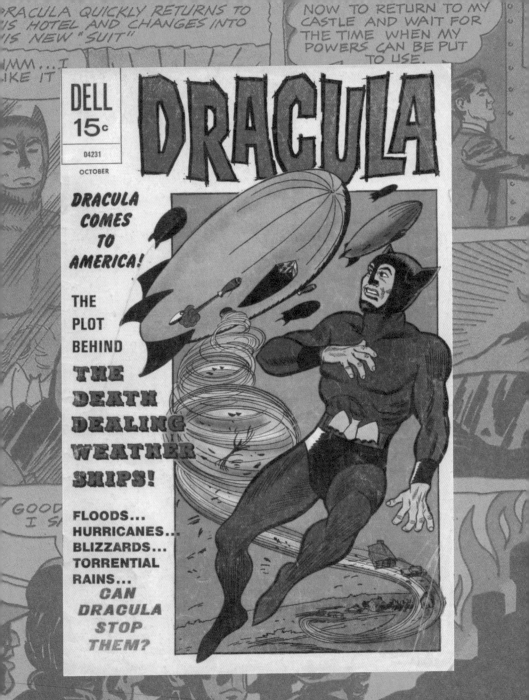

somehow my example will be an
example to all men. "

Despite his mission to restore honor to the family name, Dracula adopts a pseudonym, "Aloysius Ulysses Card," a.k.a. "Al U. Card," an impenetrable alias, providing that no one ever reads his business card backward.

As if to mimic the better-known bat-based superhero who preceded him, Dracula procures a "bat-cave" of his very own (an underground government installation and bomb shelter hidden under the grounds of an expansive family estate) and a sidekick "Fleeta" (short for "Fledermaus"). What he couldn't replicate was the longevity of either his superheroic predecessor or his gothic namesake. Despite his return via reprints, Dracula's short-lived superhero career never made it past three adventures.

EDITOR'S NOTE...

Vampires make their presence known among the superhero set with some frequency. Examples include Spider-Man's sometimes-foe/sometimes-ally Morbius the Living Vampire, the vampire-hunting Blade (himself half vampire, on his father's side), the Teen Titan called Nightrider, and the Outsiders' hypnotic Looker.

FASTER

GOOD

LITTLE FASTER

WATCH IT... PERFECT!

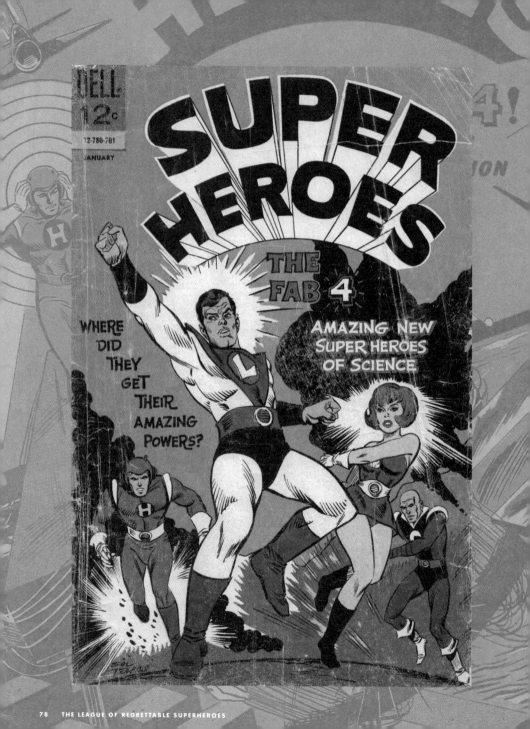

THE FAB FOUR

"Golly, Polly, girls worry about the silliest things!"

THE NAME *"THE FAB FOUR"* conjures images of a certain well-known Liverpudlian rock quartet. But during the brief existence of Dell Comics' plainly titled *Super Heroes* comic, it was also the moniker of that publisher's sole super-team.

Effecting an unusual twist on the old Captain Marvel formula—in which a child is transformed into an adult superhero—the Fab Four were sightseeing teens who happened to visit the Dell Hall of Heroes. That's right, these Dell Comics characters visited a museum dedicated to the shallow roster of superheroes from Dell Comics (specifically, the nuclear-powered pilot Nukla; Toka the Jungle King; and Kona, Monarch of Monster Isle).

The titular foursome is made up of young Southerner Reb Ogelvie, nervous nellie Tom Dennis, stalwart Danny Boyd, and Polly Wheeler, the group's sole female member. Before the friends can make it to the museum's gift shop, they're caught in a weird science explosion emanating from a nearby laboratory. The explosion somehow gives the kids the powers to transfer their minds into a quartet of android superheroes currently on display in the Hall of Heroes. Why those four android superheroes were on display is unrevealed, but it's possible they were being exhibited as examples of the worst superhero code names in history. Danny takes over the powerful robot body "El," so named for the letter on his chest (which stands for "laser"). Tom finds himself possessing the hypersonic "Hy." Forever-chilly Reb becomes the cryogenic "Crispy," and Polly becomes the frictionless "Polymer Polly," able to weave nearly unbreakable polymer strands.

A lot of questions are left unanswered. . . . Who invented these superpowered robots in the first place? Why aren't these kids in school? And where the heck *is* the Dell Hall of Heroes, anyway? During their short-lived series, Danny, Tommy, Reb, and Polly go sightseeing around America, in the course of one issue traveling from northern Pennsylvania to the Florida coast. Yet they're never so far from the Hall of Heroes that they can't immediately summon their heroic android selves when trouble arises.

It's also left to the readers' imagination to decide what happens to the teens' bodies while their minds are occupying the androids. The kids seem to be leaving their human shells in considerable danger.

The Fab Four debuted and disappeared in the short span of four issues, but they packed a lot of enemies into their schedule: the Clown, Johnny Boom Boom, the mad modernist architect Mister Nutt, Nepto the shark man, a brutal and ever-burning giant called the Coal Man, and more.

Created by:
Don Arneson
and Sal Trapiani

Debuted in:
Super Heroes #1
(Dell Comics,
January 1967)

Headquarters:
A superhero
museum that's
somehow close to
everywhere

© 1967 by Dell Comics

FATMAN THE HUMAN FLYING SAUCER

"Sorry boys ... but the scales are weighted in my favor!"

Created by:
C. C. Beck and
Otto Binder

Debuted in:
Fatman, the Human Flying Saucer #1 (Lightning Comics, April 1967)

Possible unused IDs:
Capt. Corpulent the Living UFO, Tubby Titan the Anthropomorphic Alien Vessel

C. BECK AND OTTO BINDER were two of the key personnel responsible for making the original Captain Marvel, the lightning-empowered, "Shazam!" spouting World's Mightiest Mortal, one of the most popular superheroes not only in comics but around the world. (Not to be confused with Captain Marvel the self-dismembering android, page 73). Unfortunately for this dynamic duo, in 1951 the long-running lawsuit between Captain Marvel's publisher Fawcett and rival comics publisher National Comics (home of Superman, and now known as DC Comics) was ultimately decided in favor of the Man of Steel. Beck and Binder found themselves jobless when Fawcett subsequently shut down its comics-creating wing.

The 1950s were lean years for superhero comics across the board. But in the late 1960s, the popularity of the Batman TV show revitalized interest in superheroes. It was at this point that Beck and Binder chose to reunite for another attempt to catch lightning in a bottle, as it were.

The result of their collaboration was the absurd Fatman, a plump but athletic character named Van Crawford who was happy to spend his idle time indulging his many and varied hobbies and collections. When a spaceship—also a shape-changing alien—crashes within sight of his daily constitutional, Crawford rushes to its aid. He is rewarded for his efforts with the power to transform himself into a UFO.

Decked out in a suit resembling a verdant version of Captain Marvel's famous duds, Fatman battled a roster of foes that included the titanic Anti-Man, the hideous Brainman from Mars, underground gnome Grollo, Syntho the Patchwork Man, and the lovely but evil Lunita, the Moon Witch. He was well served by both his athletic bulk and his unusual alternate persona as a living, thinking spaceship. Along the way, Fatman picked up a fellow crime-fighter, Tin Man, an unusually skinny teenager who gained himself a robot body thanks to a chemical concoction of his own invention.

Fatman, the Human Flying Saucer and partner title *Tod Holton, Super Green Beret* constituted the only output by publisher Lightning Comics, which folded after a few scant months. Since then, sightings of Fatman, like the flying saucers he emulated, have been scattered and unreliable. Lightning Comics promised one more superhero title, which it never delivered. The lawyer-baiting title of this never-made book: *Captain Shazam!*

GUNMASTER

"Get back in the train, President Grant! They're after you!"

TIMID, BESPECTACLED CLAY BOONE is despised by the woman he loves because of his cowardice. If only he could be more like that daring, masked stranger who appears in the tiny Old West town of Rawhide in times of danger!

Unbeknownst to his would-be lady love, Clay Boone—spoiler alert—*is* that masked hero, the daring duelist known as Gunmaster. Hiding behind his seemingly telling civilian career as an apprentice gunsmith, Boone is actually an avowed pacifist who only unholsters his shooters when all other attempts at peacemaking fail.

Shy on superpowers, Gunmaster gets by with an increasingly inventive arsenal of guns and gunlike gimmicks, all of his own creation. When a gun that shoots gas bombs or flares fails to solve the problem, Boone's unerring eye for trick shots makes him an admirable enemy of evil.

With the quick resolution of a shootout solving most of his problems, no small amount of the average Gunmaster adventure is spent on Boone justifying his seemingly contradictory lifestyle. When his civilian identity is accused of cowardice, he thinks to himself, "She may be right! I'm too cowardly to live by the principles I think are right."

But then he goes on to insist, "If I MUST resort to guns as they do, then I will be master of the weapon! My enemies have guns, I have better ones! They have skill … I will match that and better! If I MUST fight, then I will win!"

Gunmaster's torturous only-if-I-gotta position is a little harder to buy when Boone decides to take his gun shop on the road, seemingly seeking out trouble across the still-wild Wild West. Along the way, he picks up a kid sidekick. Bullet, the Gun Boy who, in his civilian guise of Bob Tellub (read it backward for a mediocre surprise), becomes Boone's apprentice. He also comes across a few colorful supervillains, like the wild Apache warrior Hawk, the corpulent criminal genius known as "Brains," and the hypnotic menace called "The Barker."

Despite acquiring a fledgling rogues' gallery, a kid sidekick, and a graduation to his own title, Gunmaster's guns a-blazin' faded away after a couple dozen appearances. Here's hoping he ended up in a place where he could abide by his peaceful beliefs.

Created by:
Dick Giordano

Debuted in:
Six-Gun Heroes #59
(Charlton Comics,
October 1960)

How many guns does he own?
So many guns

© 1960 by Charlton Comics

JIGSAW

"I'm lucky to be alive ... I guess."

Created by:
Joe Simon,
Otto Binder, and
Bill Draut

Debuted in:
Jigsaw #1 (Harvey
Comics, September
1966)

Level of difficulty:
Hundreds of pieces,
ages 8 and up

© 1966 by
Harvey Comics

S THE BLURB ON the cover of this hero's debut appearance warns: "Don't laugh at the Jigsaw Man!" Well, if they didn't want us to laugh, they probably shouldn't have made the Jigsaw Man look like that.

The "Man of a Thousand Parts" whose "mechanical parts make him the greatest crimefighter on Earth" begins his career in outer space. Colonel Gary Jason (having two first names is almost a guarantee that one will become a superhero of some sort), astronaut with the Earth Space Force and pilot of the exploratory orbital vessel *Stargazer One*, is caught up in a "magnetic cone" that is stealing rocks, trees, and animals from remote Siberia and depositing them on the moon. Battered and bruised by fast-moving space debris, left teetering on the edge of death, Colonel Jason is rescued by the rock-stealing but otherwise well-meaning aliens behind the phenomenon.

Eager to ensure that earthlings view them as friendly, the metallic extraterrestrials make up for their cosmic faux pas by rebuilding the badly broken astronaut (for better or worse). During a hasty operation—a sort of reverse alien autopsy—the human's broken body is replaced with gaudy multicolored plates that interlock around his limbs and torso in jigsaw fashion.

Even more alarming than Colonel Jason's new form is his exponential increase in strength and sudden stretchability. The "Moon-mile of synthetic tendons" that replaced Jason's shattered limbs are also limitlessly elastic, granting Jigsaw the power to dramatically telescope parts of his body.

Stretchy superheroes are not particularly uncommon in comic books, but Jigsaw is one of the few whose ability to elasticize his body is manifested in a genuinely unsettling manner. Rather than smoothly expanding like a rubber band, the interlocking plates on Jigsaw's body separate, allowing his ropey alien tendons to swing free. It's appropriate that Jigsaw's origin seems to borrow so much from 1960s-era sci-fi suspense programs—*The Twilight Zone* and *The Outer Limits*, for example—given that the manifestation of his power is utterly terrifying.

The Space Force is convinced that Jason has been replaced by an alien monster, while his girlfriend responds to his newly elastic existence with a prolonged shriek of horror. So, Jigsaw spends most of his subsequent adventures puzzling about in outer space. He enlists in a cosmic Cold War battle against the sinister Pulots, a conquering alien empire. Once fully assembled, Jigsaw stymies the Pulots' plans and competes in the Interplanetary Olympics. After that, Jigsaw evidently fell to pieces and hasn't yet been put back together again.

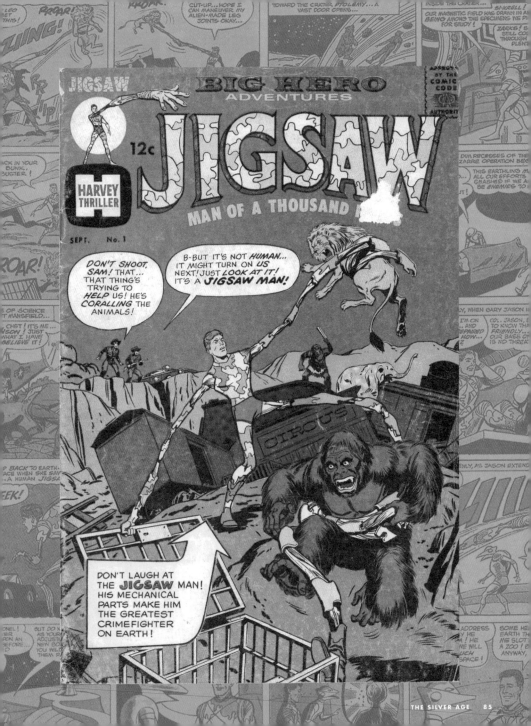

MIRACLE MAN
"Fantastic! Even I can't tell the difference!"

OMIC BOOK SUPERHEROES HAVE a long history of liberally "borrowing" from one another, which is a polite way of saying that some new characters are little more than modified copies of existing ones. In the case of "Mirakel Man"—a.k.a. "SuperHombre"—the mystery of who begat whom doesn't require a lot of detective work. This character sits in the middle of a lineage of imitators, most created by the same man, the British writer and artist Mick Anglo.

Long before SuperHombre, there was the original Captain Marvel, the popular American superhero who—his competitor's claims of copyright infringement notwithstanding—outsold even Superman during an extended period in the Golden Age of comics. The "Big Red Cheese" was equally popular overseas, and London-based publisher L. Miller & Son possessed the lucrative contract to republish the adventures of the Marvel family for U.K. audiences.

In 1953, however, the long-running lawsuit between the publishers of Superman and Captain Marvel came down in favor of the Man of Steel, drastically changing the superhero comics landscape. In the wake of the decision, publisher Fawcett ceased publication of all of its Captain Marvel–related titles and closed its comics publishing arm, a decision that left L. Miller & Son without its most popular title.

Under Mick Anglo's direction, L. Miller launched a suspiciously familiar character using the name "Marvelman." Boasting the same grinning squint and simplified linework of Captain Marvel, Marvelman even debuted under a Captain Marvel–like logo. He changed from newsboy Mickey Moran (see Captain Marvel's Billy Batson) into Marvelman by using a magic word—in this case, not "Shazam!" but "Kimota!" And in place of the Captain's youthful sidekicks—Captain Marvel Jr. and Mary Marvel—Marvelman palled around with Young Marvelman and Kid Marvelman.

In the same year, Anglo created another Shazam-alike, Captain Universe, "The Super Marvel," whose look and abilities were likewise intended to invoke the idea of Captain Marvel. In his single appearance, Captain Universe attains his powers via the magic word "GALAP," an unlikely acronym standing for Galileo (Master of the Galaxies), Archimedes (Master of Physics), Leonardo da Vinci (Master of Invention), Aristotle (Master of Philosophy), and Pythagoras (Master of Geometry).

Then, in 1958, the Spanish publisher Editorial Ferma approached Anglo to oversee the creation of a new superhero for the Spanish-language market. →

Created by:
Mick Anglo

Debuted in:
Miracle Man #1
(Thorpe & Porter, 1965)

Known relatives:
Captain Marvel, Marvelman, Super-Hombre, Mirakel Man, Miracleman

The result was "SuperHombre," another Captain Marvelesque super-hero (bearing the same name that Superman held in the Mexican market).

With both Miracleman and SuperHombre thriving in 1960, Anglo split with publisher L. Miller, though his former employers continued issuing reprinted adventures of Marvelman. Meanwhile, Anglo created still another variation on the Captain Marvel model: Captain Miracle, whose magic word of power was "El Karim" (try saying it backward). If these adventures reminded readers of the old Marvelman stories, that's because they were meant to. In fact, they were redrawn versions of those stories, with Marvelman now in a new costume.

Yet, that still wasn't the end of Anglo's marvelous variations. In 1965, he debuted Miracle Man, "the superman of unlimited power," who was SuperHombre in all but name. Transforming himself into mighty Miracle Man by means of the magic word "sundisc"—not an acronym or reversed word but, rather, a description of the emblem he bore on his chest—Miracle Man and his sometimes-sidekick Supercoat marked the end of Anglo's reinventions. He shuttered his studio, leaving unknown how many more British iterations on the original Captain Marvel might have one day existed.

EDITOR'S NOTE...

Anglo's (somewhat) original character Marvelman was revived in the 1980s. To avoid legal conflict with publisher Marvel Comics, when reprinted in the United States, Marvelman was rebranded "Miracleman." As for the character who started this whole chain, DC has given up the name Captain Marvel and rebranded him as Shazam.

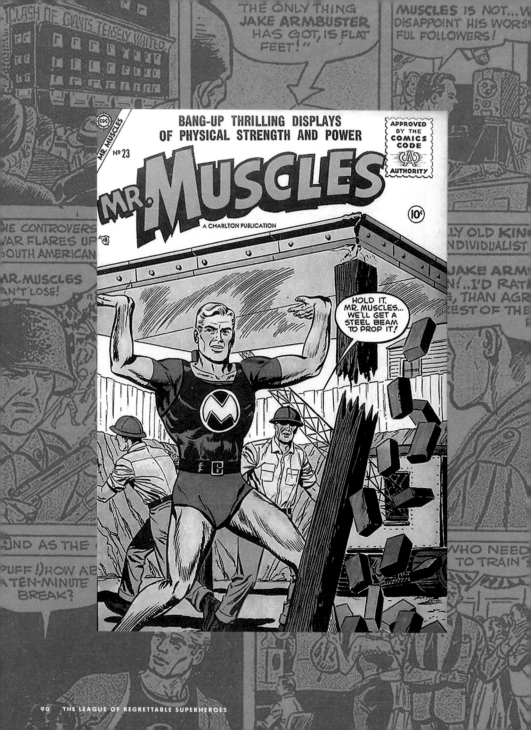

MR. MUSCLES

"Iron bars do not a prison make ... particularly if you have muscle-power!"

HE COVER TO HIS debut appearance promises "Bang-up thrilling displays of physical strength and power," while inside the book, readers are offered a glimpse at "the world's mightiest man" and "the most perfect specimen of manhood alive," a.k.a. the "greatest crusader for clean living and justice the world has ever known!" It all sounds very exciting!

Mr. Muscles is a former weakling named Brett Carson, who, a few years before the beginning of the story, was suffering advanced stages of polio. Facing imminent paralysis, Brett dedicated himself to recovering his lost mobility. During the subsequent months of struggle, he slowly recovers in small, painful bursts—he moves his fingers, he is able to sit—while receiving consistent lack of encouragement from his doctors. After being told he'll never walk again, Brett proudly strolls out of the hospital, pledging to "achieve absolute perfection!"

That perfection takes the form of Mr. Muscles, Brett's costumed alter ego (although it's more of a nickname than an actual secret identity). As Mr. Muscles, Brett uses his tremendous physical strength and peak conditioning to foil criminals and generally save the day, in true superheroic fashion. Also in the old costumed crime-fighter tradition, Mr. Muscles picks up a couple of tagalongs. Miss Muscles is a female athlete who makes only one appearance, but she seems as famous for her physical perfection as is her male counterpart. There's also Kid Muscle, Mister Muscles's sidekick, a brash and energetic youngster who spends his spare time driving around wearing a wrestling singlet, apparently looking for trouble to quash.

Despite being a physical culture advocate first and a crime-fighter second, Mr. Muscles finds himself pitted against crooks and murderers with some frequency; among his foes are carnies, the Mob, a conniving wrestler named Jake Armbuster, a red-headed Abominable Snowman (portrayed as a giant, bearded man wearing an animal skin, with no explanation where he came from), and a mad zookeeper whose envy of Mr. Muscles's physique drives him to arrange a murder-by-tiger. When not thwarting crooks and murderers, Mr. Muscles indulges crowds with displays of his tremendous strength and endurance: doing one-handed headstand pushups, bending steel bars, and allowing folks to jump off a ladder onto his stomach while he's poised in a reverse crab, then catapulting them back up to the top of the ladder. We call that one a Number Three.

Obviously intended to promote the idea of physical fitness—extreme physical fitness, even—Mr. Muscles lacked the stamina to keep it up. Two issues was the super-bodybuilder's max rep before blowout. Mr. Muscles hasn't picked up a barbell since.

Created by:
Jerry Siegel

Debuted in:
Mr. Muscles #22
(Charlton Comics,
March 1956)

Issue oddity:
Mr. Muscles took over Charlton's *Blue Beetle* comic, replacing that hero's name in the title but keeping the numbering

© 1956 by
Charlton Comics

NATURE BOY
"Let 'er rip!"

Created by:
Jerry Siegel and
John Buscema

Debuted in:
Nature Boy #3
(Charlton Comics,
March 1956)

Issue oddity:
Nature Boy took
over the numbering
of fireman hero
Danny Blaze's title

© 1956 by
Charlton Comics

ERRY SIEGEL'S MOST FAMOUS creation (with artist Joe Shuster) was, of course, Superman. But he also created dozens of other, less popular superheroes, including the Star Spangled Kid and Stripesy, Robotman, Mr. Muscles (page 91), the Spectre . . . and Nature Boy. The story of Nature Boy begins in a private plane tossed by terrible winds over a rocky sea. Inside, Myra Crandall snaps at her husband, Floyd: "You were out of your mind to take the baby and me along on a sky joyride, despite weather warnings!" "No time for recriminations," retorts her husband, as the plane nosedives into the tumultuous waves below.

Floyd and Myra are rescued by a passing fishing boat, but baby David is nowhere to be seen and is assumed drowned—that is, until he shows up unharmed at the front door of the Crandall family estate, only moments later, delivered on a gust of wind.

What happened in the interim? It seems that baby David's sinking form was intercepted by a council of gods who were hanging out underwater for no apparent reason. Taking pity on the poor infant, the deities adopt him as their own and then return him to his family home (evidently, *adoption* means something different to supernatural figureheads).

David grows up to become Nature Boy, a crusader for good entrusted with a fraction of the powers of his adopted godparents, only a few of whom are familiar to anyone who gave Edith Hamilton's *Mythology* a passing glance. There's the well-known Neptune, but also Gusto (god of the air), Fura (ruler of fire), Eartha (who, predictably enough, rules the earth), and then Allura, Azura, Electra, and Friga, who command the realms of love, sky, electricity, and cold. His title also featured the appearance of Nature Man—possibly Nature Boy as an adult—and Nature Girl, who protected the jungle by wielding the powers of gravity.

Unusual for a superhero, Nature Boy needed to appeal to his benefactors to deliver the tools to fight crime and injustice: lightning bolts (which he was able to ride), powerful winds, earthquakes, and so on. Pretty much the only power David seemed to have acquired on his own is the ability to change back and forth between his heroic and civilian identities, which he does in a flash (accompanied by his genuinely odd, if enthusiastic, exclamation, "Let 'er rip!"). He was, in short, one of the few superheroes who had to ask permission to use his powers.

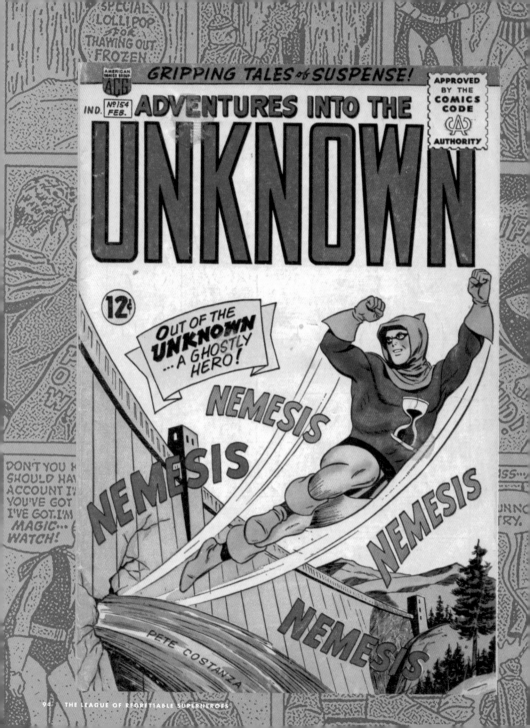

NEMESIS

"Make way for Nemesis!"

EFORE THEY CAN BEGIN their crime-fighting careers, some superheroes have to endure the most harrowing origin of all. First, they have to die. One of these postmortal paladins was Nemesis, formerly a police detective with the hardboiled name Steve Flint. While pursuing a murderous saboteur and mob boss named Goratti, Flint is run over by a train. End of story? No! Promptly dispatched to the afterlife, a green-tinted other-dimensional home of the dead called "The Unknown," Flint takes the opportunity of a backlogged admissions system to formally request that he be allowed to return to earth to avenge his own murder.

A newly hired Grim Reaper, himself a victim of Goratti's homicidal tendencies, not only allows Flint's request but also outfits him with a costume designed to strike terror into the hearts of criminals: striped shorts and a T-shirt with a hood. Well, we did say Death was new at the job.

The freshly christened Nemesis does so well at his new calling—one-upping his own death by pushing Goratti into the path of a blazing rocket exhaust—that the Reaper allows him to retain his striped pants of office and continue defending the world of the living from murderers and crooks. In the tradition of the undead superhero, Nemesis is gifted with a series of powers so broadly defined as to render him omnipotent. Naturally, he can fly and possesses remarkable strength, and of course he could turn invisible and walk through walls, just like any other ghost. In addition, when necessary, Nemesis could also change his size, read minds, and travel through time.

All these powers came with limitations, however. Despite being dead, Nemesis still apparently had to breathe, and so he had to be wary of poison gas and drowning. More important, exposure to excessively strong illumination turned Nemesis into a powerless weakling, vulnerable to mortal weapons.

Life wasn't all duty and danger. Nemesis had a mortal earthly girlfriend, Lita Revelli Craig, although the Grim Reaper disapproved of the relationship (isn't that always the way?) and the couple had a tendency to argue (ditto). When taking time off from his duties, Nemesis retired to a high-rise apartment in one of the Unknown's swankier ZIP codes.

After a respectable few years battling evil on earth while balancing the ultimate in long-distance relationships, Nemesis hung up his hood for good. Presumably, he retired to the Unknown, where he is still waiting for his death certificate to be processed.

Created by:
Richard E. Hughes (as "Zev Zimmer") and Pete Costanza

Debuted in:
Adventures into the Unknown #154 (American Comics Group, February 1965)

Tailor:
Tim Burton, apparently

© 1965 by American Comics Group

PEACEMAKER

"Nerve gas ... quicker than bullets ... and not as fatal!"

Created by:
Joe Gill and
Pat Boyette

Debuted in:
Fightin' 5 #40
(Charlton Comics,
November 1966)

**Likely helmet
inspirations:**
A meatloaf pan,
a compost bin,
the Getty

© 1966 by
Charlton Comics

EACEMAKER WAS FAMOUSLY "the man who loves peace so much that he is willing to fight for it," or at least so the cover blurb on his first issue would have us believe. Arguably, that description applies to pretty much every superhero. What else are they fighting for, if not peace? Well, Peacemaker took the fight to a different level. For the most part, he didn't fight super-villains or rampaging monsters. His rogues' gallery was populated not by people but by nations.

Secretly Christopher Smith, a "peace envoy and diplomat," the Peacemaker is also a brilliant innovator of assorted nonlethal weaponry. Outfitted with a level of armaments one might normally associate with a small country, Smith wages a one-man war on would-be world conquerors, petty tyrants, and one of comics' rare Mad Doomsday Preppers.

Why does he do it? "Because man is civilized, governed by law," Smith explains, "but unfortunately there are madmen who will not obey those laws, and will not submit to the sanity of diplomacy!" To stay the hand of war and put down trouble-stirring dictators before innocent civilians suffer, the Peacemaker behaves like "an 'Action-Buffer' between these madmen and global war!"

Inspired by the example of his parents—his father was a soldier, statesman, and adventurer; his mother was a research scientist—Smith develops an array of varied skills, ranging from spear-fishing to engineering, and creates his own personal arsenal of undeadly arms. He carried a gun with fired "medicated pellets" to stun his enemies insensate, plus knockout gas that could be fired "at supersonic speeds." His credo: end conflicts with nonviolent solutions (although he apparently didn't count "tremendous explosions" as violence).

Despite his lofty ambitions, the Peacemaker is remembered primarily for wearing a helmet that resembled a toilet seat. As a matter of fact, the helmet—and his entire costume—was packed with weaponry. The helmet held a laser and was impregnated with high explosives and a hidden fuse; his gloves became fire bombs when a secret vial sewn into them was crushed; the heels of his boots were densely packed plastic explosives; even his shirt was woven of highly flammable material. Basically, the Peacemaker was always an errant spark away from exploding into a million bits.

THE SENTINELS
"Togetherness is for the birds, baby!"

Created by:
Gary Friedrich and
Sam Grainger

Debuted in:
Thunderbolt vol.
3, #54 (Charlton
Comics, October
1966)

**Current
whereabouts:**
Probably "on the
road" (get it?)

© 1966 by
Charlton Comics

MID ALL THE OTHER prominent crazes of the mid-1960s—the jet age, the space race, super-spies, and Batman-inspired high camp—the Sentinels hold the distinction of cornering the superhero market in the burgeoning counterculture beat movement. While other costumed crime-fighters held day jobs as scientists, reporters, and idle millionaires, the Sentinels were an up-and-coming trio of protest singers, a sort of superheroic Peter, Paul, and Mary.

As "The Protestors" performing such cheerful ditties as "The Doomsday Dirge" (sample lyric: "The doomsday dirge, the doubters we'll purge") and folksy jailhouse hits (daring censure with hard-hitting lyrics, like "Then I threw a pie in the Warden's face . . . "), the Sentinels' three members turned a typical comic book convention on its head. In their civilian identities, they wore domino masks as part of their musical gimmick, like a really toned-down KISS.

The Sentinels may also be the only superhero team to gain powers from their landlord. The elderly "Mr. Jones" (actually "Kolotov"), secretly a brilliant Russian scientist who fled the Soviets, hands his young lodgers super-scientific outfits that give them amazing powers. Front man Rick Strong becomes the high-flying Helio, lovely Cindy Carson becomes the telepathic Mentalia, and big lug "Crunch" Wilson becomes the hard-hitting Brute.

The Sentinels spend as much time arguing among themselves as they do fighting evil. And though their benefactor's deathbed remit was to battle the spread of communism, they spend most of their energy tackling a hooded world-beater named Mind-Bender and his android assistant, the Titan. Frankly, it's probably for the best that they limited their opposition to smaller targets because they weren't particularly good at superhero-ing. At one point, Helio takes a bump on the head that renders him a confused amnesiac for a full third of the Sentinels' few adventures together.

The most unfortunate aspect of the Sentinels, though, is that the beatnik gimmick isn't followed through. All three have fame and fortune on their mind, they hate communism, and they're downright deferential to authority figures. What kind of protestors are these? As the band sings:

> *Got me a great big explodin' bomb*
> *Fixin' to drop it on Viet Nam*
> *But I lost my way and instead*
> *I dropped it on my uncle's head!*

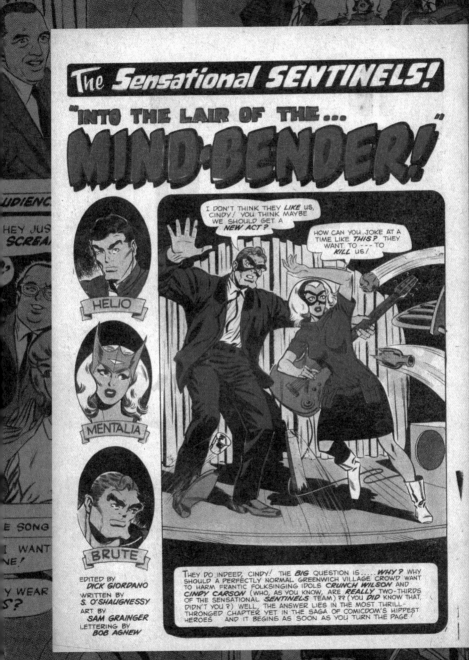

SPYMAN

"Maybe I can't fire a lightning bolt but ... what's to keep me from making like Gorgeous George!"

AMES BOND MAY HAVE been the secret agent with all the best gadgets, but this comic book counterespionage counterpart had him beat in terms of convenience. Spyman carried his entire arsenal of slick spy goodies in his *artificial robot hand*!

Spyman is secretly Johnny Chance, agent of the American counterintelligence organization known only as LIBERTY (an acronym so secret that not even the reader is told what it stands for). Disarming a nuclear bomb set by enemy agents, our man Chance manages to save thousands of lives by removing the bomb's radioactive core, but at the cost of his left hand.

In a fantastic stroke of luck, the radioactivity that destroyed his hand altered his cellular structure, allowing miracle surgery that would otherwise fail. The result: Agent Chance wakes up with a cybernetic left hand, which is packed with gadgets and deadly weapons. Imagine!

Spyman's cybernetic "Electro Robot Hand" contains pretty much everything a jet-age super-spy might need. Diagrams in every issue of his comic outline the specifics. There's an X-Ray probe, a recording device, and an "electro-blast unit"; one finger is capable of emitting "the black ray," an all-obscuring beam of pure darkness. And if one of the Electro Robot Hand's built-in fingers doesn't do the trick, he can swap in a new one. "The pouches on this belt hold spare fingers" explains Spyman's fellow agent Dr. Vane, describing the world's most unsettling fashion accessory.

As secret spy organizations go, LIBERTY doesn't invest all that heavily in secrecy. For one thing, it maintains its headquarters inside the Statue of Liberty, where, one would imagine, tourists might notice all the helicopters flying in and out of the torch. And for another thing, the official LIBERTY agent uniform—Spyman's included—is a skintight bright-red bodysuit that would stand out even on the streets of New York City.

Still, Spyman and his pals at LIBERTY manage to defeat weird villains like the ID Machine, Cyclops, and the Whisperer as well as evil organizations like the Evil Eye Society and MIRAGE (possibly the only group in the world to use a reverse acronym: the Empire of Guerilla Assassination, Revenge, and International Menace).

Despite featuring some of the very first comic book art from comics legend Jim Steranko, Spyman and his Electro Robot Hand failed to grab a significant fan following. After three appearances, he folded up his bright-red jumpsuit, packed away his extra fingers, and left for parts unknown. Possibly, he's trying his hand at a less conspicuous career.

Created by:
Joe Simon and
Jim Steranko

Debuted in:
Spyman #1
(Harvey Comics,
September 1966)

Additional secret agent gadgets:
Spare house key, can opener, dog whistle

© 1966 by Harvey Comics

PART THREE

THE MODERN AGE
1970 – PRESENT

AS THE 1970S DAWNED, SUPERHEROES HAD begun to emerge from their adolescence and were ready to grow up. Where it had once been sufficient for a caped crime-fighter to keep his do-goodery confined to super-villains and the occasional agent of an enemy nation, superheroes increasingly found themselves directly addressing problems related to social issues. Drug abuse, civil rights, and profound existential dilemmas became as much the purview of the genre as radioactive eyebeams and bulletproof skin.

As the stories grew more serious, the violence levels ramped up as well, and superheroes of the 1980s onward were often part of a "grim and gritty" universe. An entire decade-plus of furious, bloodthirsty, and heavily armored heroes became the norm, a legacy that lingers today. On the positive side, the independent comics scene has flourished. More sophisticated storytelling, including such high-profile critical successes as Alan Moore and Dave Gibbons's *Watchmen*, encouraged a new generation of innovative writers and artists to invent some of the most fascinating, thoughtful, well-crafted superhero tales ever produced. We won't be talking about them, though . . .

NOTE: Comic book historians often subdivide this period into a Bronze Age that begins with the socially relevant stories of the mid-1970s, followed by a Modern Age that starts with the grimmer tales of the mid-1980s.

ADAM-X — THE X-TREME
"Burn!"

Created by:
Fabian Nicieza
and Tony Daniel

Debuted in:
X-Force Annual #2
(Marvel Comics,
October 1993)

**Alternate unused
identities:**
Ricky X the R-X-dical, Artie X the
A-X-esome

© 1993 by Marvel Comics

S FAR AS THE world of comics is concerned, in the 1990s everything became extreme. Until then, the typical superhero could get by with a flashy set of superpowers, a bright costume, and a clear ethical code. But the twentieth century's last decade or so put a radical, outrageous, Cool Ranch–flavored spin on comics characters, adding blades, goatees, overcoats, amorality, and attitude to everyone and everything.

Enter Adam X, "The X-Treme," as radical as a pair of surf pants kicking a rad ollie on a skateboard. He's the most 1990s-est superhero ever produced by the House of Ideas—and that's saying a lot, considering that Marvel Comics all but created the trend in the first place. In 1990, the company introduced Cable, a tough-as-nails telekinetic mutant cyborg commando from a postapocalyptic future, effectively launching the decade's fascination with big guns, padded armor, and characters with tiny, tiny feet. When Cable's cocreator Rob Liefeld and others left Marvel to help found rival Image Comics, the elder company suddenly found itself needing to play catchup. Marvel had no choice but to try a few of its own hard-hitting, unforgiving, and willing-to-kill characters.

Adam-X was the apotheosis of the idea: a half-alien, half-mutant rebel from space, whose culture wasn't so foreign that it hadn't developed the backward baseball cap as a fashion statement. Also affixing Adam-X to his decade was a leonine mullet and a robust "soul patch" branding his chin. But mostly he was all about the edge; indeed, Adam-X's distinctive costume was festooned with cutting blades. Seriously, they were protruding from his shoulders, lining the outside of his gloves, sticking out from his hands, strapped around his arms and thighs, arranged in a ring around his belt, and jutting out from his kneepads. The guy was a one-man knife shop, and that isn't even counting his "Thet'je" blades, enormous double-bladed hooks he wielded with both hands. If Wolverine was cool because he had claws, then Adam-X was surely ten times as awesome!

Of course, a reasonable explanation for his knifery does exist: his mutant power relied on cutting his opponents. Adam-X possessed the unsettling ability to ignite the blood from any open wound on mental command, literally causing his opponent's blood to boil. Radical, indeed!

As the decade died down, so, too, did readers' collective fascination with heavily armed, heavily bladed superheroes clad in black leather. With little to support the character except his seemingly by-the-numbers adherence to the zeitgeist, Adam-X bowed out in quiet, and truly unradical, fashion.

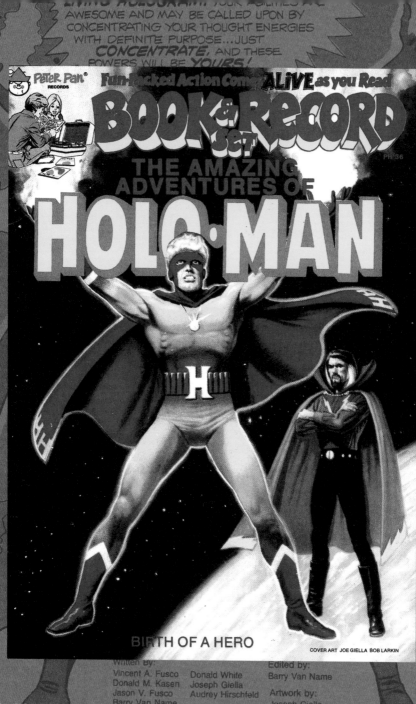

HOLO-MAN

"Those poor tourists look like they've just seen a ghost! Better concentrate and ... become ... invisible?!!"

CIENCE-BASED SUPERHEROES ARE nothing new, but the creators of Holo-Man threw pretty much every high-tech gimmick they could find into the character. This multicolored masked man was the product of not only the hologram from which he borrowed his name, but also lasers, "thermo-nuclear fusion," and the power of audio.

Peter Pan Records had experienced terrific success with a series of book-and-record sets aimed at children. Pairing illustrated storybooks with vinyl LPs, which contained sound effects, music, and dramatic readings of the story so that children could read along, the company primarily produced licensed products. The Peter Pan catalog was rife with properties from television shows, films, cartoons, and, in no small amount, superhero comic books. After a few years of producing audio adventures for everyone from Spider-Man and Batman to Man-Thing and Metamorpho, Peter Pan decided to try marketing an original superhero of its own making: enter, Holo-Man!

The story begins as noted "laser physicist" Dr. James Robinson plays host to the president of the United States at the "Top secret U.S. Government Laser Development Complex." Suddenly, saboteurs strike, just as Dr. Robinson is in the middle of demonstrating a revolutionary new fuel source powered by "laser induced thermo-nuclear fusion." The machines housing the lasers explode. Robinson narrowly saves the president's life but, in doing so, is disintegrated.

I know what you're thinking, but that's not the end of the story! At this point, the soon-to-be Holo-Man's origin comes fast and furious (and ridiculous). The good doctor is somehow encased safely in a nearby, life-sized holographic plate, which is then shunted into another "dimensional plateau" somewhere within something called a "mind-aura," where a bearded and cloaked figure named "Laserman" grants Robinson tremendous powers that are controlled by a "holodisc" from a "future time dimension." (Good thing these quote marks are sold in bulk.) The gibberish gets even thicker as Laserman charges Holo-Man with his mission:

"The coherent laser beams converge within your body and transform you into the world's first living hologram! Your abilities are awesome, and may be called upon by concentrating your thought-energies with definite purpose . . . just concentrate and these powers will be yours!" The bearded space wizard encourages Holo-Man to "engage the forces of evil in battles from which the preservation of good must triumph and the suffering of mankind shall be eased from the world!"

Created by:
Vincent A. Fusco and Donald M. Kasen

Debuted in:
The Amazing Adventures of Holo-Man (Peter Pan Records, 1978)

Not to be confused with:
T. S. Elliot's Hollow Man, Hulu.com, Hello Kitty

© 1978 by Peter Pan Records

→

That's one tall order for a man dressed like a melting Popsicle. Decked out in an outfit resembling a bad accident at a tie-dye shirt factory, Holo-Man attempts to save America from an attack by insidious "Surrian" invaders. (What, the Russians weren't available? Oh, wait, I get it.) He's equipped with powers of invisibility, illusion-making, and "molecular teleportation"—which, one assumes, is the same as plain old teleportation.

Holo-Man's inaugural adventure ends on a quite a cliffhanger: thousands of holographic Surrian nuclear missiles rain down from the skies over Washington, D.C., leaving our hero mere seconds to prevent utter panic from sweeping the streets. My guess is he somehow does it with holograms.

The series was obviously intended to continue after Holo-Man's solo holo-showing. Besides ending on the pre-apocalyptic cliffhanger mentioned above, the book featured a full-page pinup introducing the audience to Holo-Man's allies, most of whom had yet to be introduced. Along with Laserman, the "Holo Squad" consisted of the regal and tiara-topped Utopia, the youthful Wavelength and his animal pets, and a clipboard-wielding Laserwoman. Also featured was a lightning-framed, purple-shirted figure who most likely would have turned out to be Holo-Man's archnemesis, had the book (and record) managed to last beyond a single appearance.

MORLOCK 2001

"I like the birds because they are so free!"

Created by:
Michael Fleischer
and Al Milgrom

Debuted in:
Morlock 2001 #1
(Atlas Comics,
February 1975)

Care instructions:
Plant 12 inches
apart, full to
partial sun

© 1975 by Atlas Comics

HE LEAD CHARACTER OF *Morlock 2001* may have the most ignoble origin in the history of comics. While other heroes launched their careers from fantastic alien worlds, high-tech laboratories, or your average island paradise, Morlock started life as . . . an eggplant.

Proving that heroes are not only born or made but also sometimes harvested, Morlock was the product of forbidden horticultural experiments in the far-flung dystopian future, the year 2001. Confiscated by the brutally repressive regime of the world government, the pods containing Morlock and his unhatched siblings revealed plant-human hybrids—beings who looked like men, but whose bodies were made of a strange "Fibro-Cellular Structure."

Morlock emerges from his cocoon fully grown, possessing the power of speech, a human form, and a pointy white hairstyle that makes him look like the mascot for a brand of soft-serve ice cream. Evidently that is exactly the kind of breakthrough the government has been looking for because they quickly indoctrinate the plant-man into their ranks.

Government life doesn't suit Morlock, particularly since the gentle man-plant loves peace and can't wrap his rutabaga around the actions of the repressive regime that pays his celery—er, *salary*. In fact, as a superhero, Morlock doesn't do much except look awfully good compared to the excesses of the futuristic government. Unless, that is, you make him angry.

Like the Hulk, during moments of stress the gentle Morlock transforms into a terrifying, mindless, super-strong monster. Unlike the original comic book man-monster, however, Morlock doesn't just hop around racking up property damage and mangling the spoken word. He eats people! When his violent alter ego takes over, Morlock, looking to all the world like a walking radish made out of beef jerky, is just as likely to kill and consume his allies as his enemies.

After two issues, the decision came down that Morlock had gone about as far as a man-eating vegetable could conceivably go. With his third issue title amended to add "and The Midnight Men," Morlock meets the leader of said group, who is called "The Midnight Man." Wanted by the government, the Midnight Man doesn't take long to realize that an uncontrollable fern that feeds on human beings is less an asset than a hindrance. With government agents bearing down on him, the Midnight Man puts a bullet in his newfound ally. He then proceeds to blow himself up, along with his men and his headquarters, because "better death than slavery!" How the story may have resolved from there is anyone's guess. Atlas-Seaboard folded shortly thereafter.

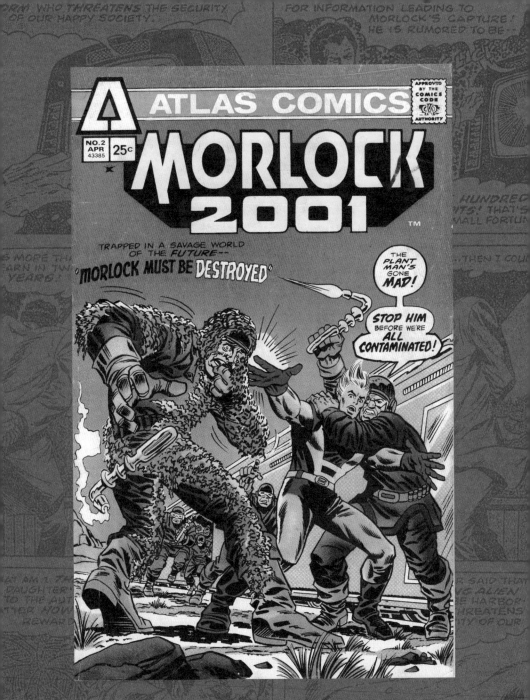

THE OUTSIDERS

"Let's face it ... I'm a FREAK!"

THEY'RE A TEAM OF weird-looking mutants who fight for a world that hates and fears them, banded together to protect their own from the often deadly prejudice they face merely for being . . . different. Surely it's the X-Men, right? Nope! We're talking about the Outsiders, a team of outlandish superheroes who made a sole outing in the mid-1970s. "The world's not ready for you yet!" cries a figure on the cover, and he was clearly right.

A quintet (plus a midissue addition) of self-described "freaks," the Outsiders resembled the outlandish designs of hot-rod artist Ed "Big Daddy" Roth more than strait-laced crime-fighters. The team was made up of Amazing Ronnie (a four-armed green-skinned Cyclops), Lizard Johnny (a squinting, bespectacled frog-man who could regrow damaged limbs), the immensely strong Mighty Mary (a gorgeous sloe-eyed blonde—from the collar up, anyway; below the neckline, she sported thick fish-scaled limbs), and Hairy Larry, a.k.a. "The Wheeler Dealer" (the team's wheel man—literally! Larry is somehow bonded to the truck that transports the Outsiders and bears their team logo).

The Outsiders even have a theme song, although it's surprisingly specific to the young weirdo they save from an angry mob: "Hang in there Billy . . . it's US . . . US . . . We're the Outsiders!" they sing before introducing each member and leaping into the fray. ("Billy" is a toddler sporting a gigantic bald head the size of a foot locker and is harder than steel!)

Leading the Outsiders is "Ol' Doc Scary," a fright-faced cyborg. The good doctor lost his handsome features after returning from a botched space mission to investigate alien "laser signals." Why NASA sent a surgeon to check in on alien broadcasts is anyone's guess, but the result is that Doc returns . . . changed. Having crashed on the world where the alien signals originated, Doc is rebuilt by extraterrestrials who give him eerily precise and fast cybernetic hands and a hideously disfigured face. (This origin story is similar to that of Jigsaw, another Joe Simon character highlighted on page 84.)

Hiding his horrifying new appearance under a latex mask, Doc recruits other "Freaks" to hang out with him in his lavish private quarters, a sprawling secret headquarters twenty stories below the hospital. The team didn't last, but parent company DC Comics repurposed their name about a decade later for a roster of outcasts and C-listers assembled by Batman. That group developed various incarnations, while the original Outsiders are probably still huddled around the television in their subbasement two miles below the surface of the earth.

Created by:
Joe Simon and
Jerry Grandenetti

Debuted in:
First Issue Special
#10 (DC Comics,
January 1976)

Primary problems:
Low self-esteem,
rampaging mobs

© 1976 by DC Comics

PHOENIX THE PROTECTOR

"I guess I always knew mankind would manage to destroy itself someday ... "

Created by:
Jeff Rovin and
Sal Amendola

Debuted in:
Phoenix #1
(Atlas Comics,
January 1975)

**Not to be
confused with:**
Phoenix, a.k.a. Jean
Grey; Phoenix, AZ;
the University of
Phoenix

© 1975 by Atlas Comics

N THE FAR-DISTANT FUTURE of 1977, disaster strikes the orbital space station *Threshold I.* The astronauts make an emergency evacuation, and their escape pod crashes in the Arctic. One survivor, Ed Tyler, is left freezing upon the ice.

Fortunately, Tyler's plight is noticed by the Deiei, a race of seemingly all-powerful aliens. Rescuing him from certain death, the extraterrestrials inform him that they are responsible for the evolution of humankind. They then shock the astronaut by announcing that because humanity is too violent and flawed to be allowed to continue to exist, they plan to destroy the very race they helped create. Making a break for it, Tyler helps himself to an alien spacesuit loaded with "atomic transistors" that convey tremendous powers. He then becomes the Phoenix, humanity's superpowered savior!

Phoenix is known as a surprisingly depressing comic; even the title character finds himself succumbing to pessimism. "The planet is doomed," he thinks, adding, "and I share the grim responsibility" before using his powers to carve a mountain into a king-sized gravestone for humanity that reads: "R.I.P. Planet Earth 1977."

Phoenix may be best remembered, however, for explicitly portraying its hero as a Christ-like figure. In the second issue, Phoenix describes himself as "a man to lead them away from evil—to show them the path to salvation!" With the sun creating a halo behind his head, Tyler adds, "As did I, so will man rise from the ashes of hatred and prejudice! For I am . . . PHOENIX!" He goes on to fight a sinister Deiei tyrant who calls himself "Satan" and, later, parts the waters of the Hudson River.

In its fourth issue, the editorial powers-that-be decided to turn the book's glum, foreboding tone on its ear. Helpful aliens intervene, calling themselves the Protectors of the Universe. They promptly rid the planet of the Deiei and outfit Phoenix with new clothes, fresh powers, and a novel identity.

The Protectors send Tyler (now known as "Phoenix the Protector," certainly not because competitor Marvel Comics already boasted a superhero named Phoenix, right?) back to earth to serve as the planet's guardian. Their new mission comes with a warning, though. "The moment you show hatred, bigotry, greed or any of the other human plagues," they explain, "Mankind will be doomed!" Gulp.

Luckily for humanity, the Phoenix doesn't have long to ponder the seriousness of his new mission. Its publisher Atlas Comics folded promptly after the book's fourth issue.

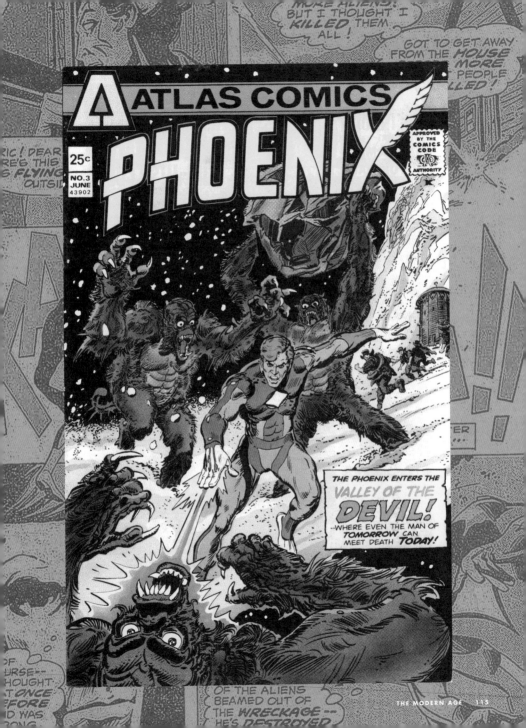

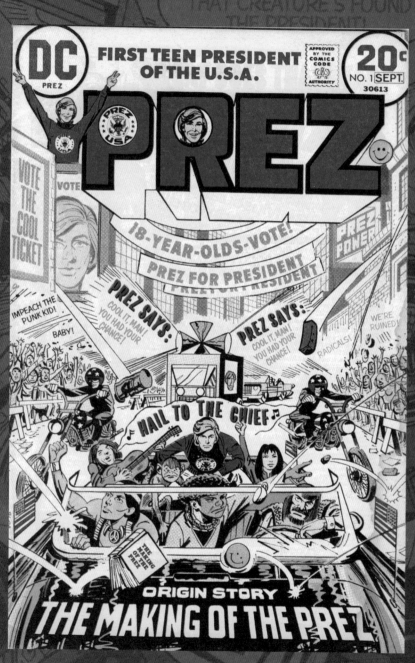

PREZ

"One thing bothers me—if the clocks aren't on time, how do we know when it's election day?"

THE YEAR IS 1973, and America is in turmoil. The wounds of Vietnam, the Watergate scandal, PONG's release, the birth of Carson Daly . . . it is, in many ways, the country's darkest hour. Surely, the only hope lies in electing a clock-obsessed teenager to be president of the United States.

Prez (a.k.a. "First Teen President") was the brainchild of Joe Simon, the man who, along with Jack "King" Kirby, created literally thousands of pages of comics and dozens of superheroes, including the paterfamilias of the patriotic superhero set, Captain America. Now teamed with artist Jerry Grandenetti, Simon was ushering in a completely new kind of patriotic superhero.

Prez Rickard is the favorite son of the modest burg of Steadfast, a town adorned with hundreds—maybe thousands—of beautifully crafted clocks. Unfortunately, no two of them keep the same time. One by one, with focus and dedication, Prez fixes all the clocks of Steadfast. This herculean task brings him to the attention of Boss Smiley, a round-headed wretch whose cartoonishly grinning mug resembles the insipid smiley face button made popular in the '70s. Seeing an opportunity, Smiley endorses the immensely popular twenty-one-year-old (yes, the "Teen President" tagline lied) for a career as the youngest senator in the United States and, following a shoved-through constitutional amendment, the youngest president in history.

Eventually, Prez rejects Boss Smiley's control, aided by his Native American pal Eagle Free, a friend to animals and director of the FBI. Prez and his administration go on to defend the U.S.A. from many familiar threats. There are assassination attempts, rabble-rousing activists, contrarian members of Congress, legless vampires, giant evil robot chess pieces—you know, the kind of day-in day-out struggles typically faced by any world leader.

For all the werewolves and robots, the real villain is the status quo. Simon used Prez to represent the idealism of baby boomer culture versus the business-as-usual protocol of success-hungry career politicians, power-craving quislings, and influential figures all too eager to turn traitor against the highest ideals of the nation. In an unpublished story, Prez even got to take on the Watergate scandal, liberating Washington, D.C., from a dual plague of "bugs" (both the electronic kind and the more familiar vermin type).

The allegory-rich story of Prez was effortlessly adapted in an issue of Neil Gaiman's well-regarded 1990s series *The Sandman*. Prez was recast as a Christ-like figure resisting the temptation of a satanic Boss Smiley. It's a shame Prez hasn't made a substantial return since. The world can never have enough heroes who stand for truth, justice, and the American Way.

Created by:
Joe Simon and
Jerry Grandenetti

Debuted in:
Prez #1 (DC
Comics, August/
September 1973)

Political affiliation:
Groovy

© 1973 by DC Comics

ROM, SPACEKNIGHT

"This sector is cleansed of Dire Wraiths! But my quest goes on!"

Created by:
Bing McCoy
(toy),
Bill Mantlo,
Sal Buscema
(comic)

Debuted in:
Rom #1
(Marvel Comics,
December 1979)

Accessories:
9-volt battery,
not included

© 1979 by Marvel Comics

ROM, A.K.A. "ROM, SPACEKNIGHT," remains an interesting conundrum in the world of comics. Despite that his long-lived comic remains a fan favorite, he will probably never again see the light of day.

When board-game manufacturer Parker Brothers decided to enter the lucrative late-1970s action figure market, competitor Kenner had opened up the market in an unprecedented way with its popular lines dedicated to the Star Wars franchise. So Parker Brothers launched its own intergalactic hero, a silver-plated robot from outer space named Rom.

The toy, manufactured cheaply and panned in a notorious *Time* magazine review, sold in disappointing numbers. But the comic book that Marvel Comics produced under license became a smash hit. Creating a backstory for Rom out of whole cloth and a few clues planted in the advertisement for the toy (which repeatedly stressed that children should only "pretend" that Rom could detect and fight evil), writer Bill Mantlo envisioned a conflict that spanned the universe.

A cyborg Spaceknight of the planet Galador, Rom has spent two centuries in an interplanetary conflict with the Dire Wraiths, a race of shape-shifting alien sorcerers. His crusade takes him to earth, where he discovers that the Dire Wraiths have adopted human form and integrated themselves into society, poised to destroy it from within.

No problem for Rom, though. The "Analyzer," one of his three toy accessories—sorry, "spaceknight weapons"—can detect Dire Wraiths in whatever form they possess. Rom's "Neutralizer" condemns them to a hellish "Shadow Zone." Unfortunately, the process leaves behind something strikingly similar to charred human remains. So, for all the human population knows, Rom is nothing more than a maniacal robot that arbitrarily turns people into smoking ash with a weird gun!

The comic book Rom was a talkative sort, even though his plastic incarnation was limited to an electronic fusillade of beeps, gongs, and labored breathing, so eventually he is able to explain his actions. He develops a supporting cast, including a love interest and a coterie of Spaceknight comrades (Trapper, Breaker, Scanner, Seeker, Starshine, Terminator, Hammerhand, and the unfortunately named Gloriole). Unfortunately, as well remembered as the series was, licensing obstacles make it unlikely that the original issues will ever be collected in a contemporary format, meaning that Rom's comic book adventures remain a rare and tantalizing find exclusive to back issue bins.

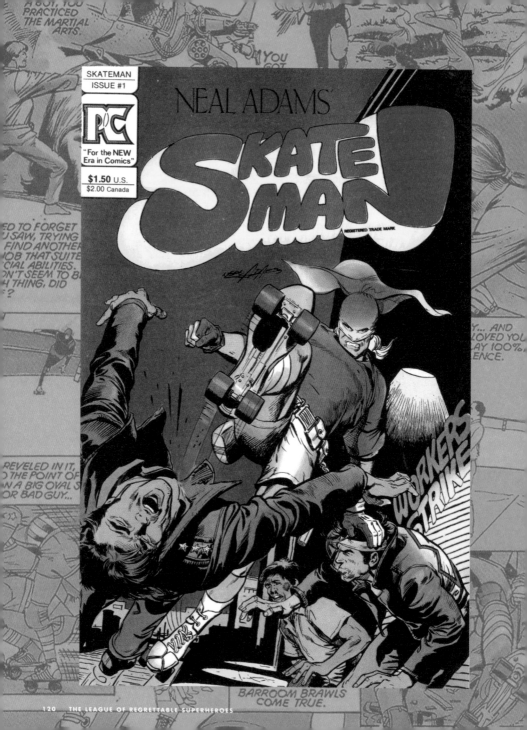

SKATEMAN

"Hands off, jerkhole! ... We're forming a union! My foot and your face!"

T'S A FAMILIAR STORY: martial artist Billy Moon returns from Vietnam to find that only roller derby can quell the turmoil in his soul. Unfortunately, Billy inadvertently crosses a branch of the mafia that apparently maintains an interest in the fortunes of the derby world (the dreaded Skate Mob, perhaps?). Soon he finds himself framed for the in-rink death of his closest pal, Jack.

Worse yet, when Billy begins to heal his wounded heart with the help of the beautiful blonde Angel, a biker gang swings by on a whim and slashes her to death with knives. It's a violent world Billy Moon inhabits, and he quickly takes to heart the maxim of an eye for an eye, and a roller-skate wheel kicking out another person's eye, and then more roller skates kicking different people in their assorted faces and eyes . . . for an eye.

Inspired by a young acquaintance's comic book collection, Billy decides to adopt the identity of a masked vigilante to avenge his friends' deaths. Looking back on the skills learned in his years of military service and lifelong study of the martial arts, he decides to base his costumed identity on roller skating, naturally. Thus, Skateman is born.

Created by comics legend Neal Adams, the *Skateman* publication boasts impeccable art but, unfortunately, questionable everything else. (Adams's more celebrated work includes iconic runs on the X-Men, Avengers, Deadman, Batman, and the groundbreaking Green Lantern/Green Arrow, plus tireless campaigning for comics creators' rights.) Allegedly developed as a tie-in for a potential licensing project, the book's ultraviolent storyline and objectionable language made it an unlikely candidate to sell whatever it was intended to market: roller skates, men's roller derby, headscarves, the mafia, whatever. Foul-mouthed, perpetually angry, and wildly irresponsible (at the climax of the book, Billy Moon gleefully sends his prepubescent assistant Paco into the bad guys' headquarters sporting a fanny pack full of live grenades), Skateman seems an unlikely choice to grace any product's packaging or advertising except, possibly, Prozac.

A low point in its creator's long and otherwise celebrated career, Skateman also has the honor of being one of the few street-level vigilantes in the history of comics to have taken justice into his own hands while wearing pristine white booty shorts. When *Skateman* #1—the first and only issue of Billy Moon's saga—ends abruptly on a climactic explosion, it's practically a blessing.

Created by:
Neal Adams

Debuted in:
Skateman #1
(Pacific Comics,
November 1983)

Signature move:
Arming minors
with grenades

© 1983 by Pacific Comics

THE SUPER SONS OF BATMAN AND SUPERMAN
"Clark baby—we must be flippin' ... "

Created by:
Bob Haney and
Dick Dillin

Debuted in:
*World's Finest
Comics* vol. 1, #215
(DC Comics,
January 1973)

Groovy quotient:
Actually, they're
both pretty square

© 1973 by DC Comics

B Y 1973, SUPERMAN AND BATMAN had been around for more than thirty years. The kids who'd read the heroes' original adventures were now in their forties and had families of their own. So, in an attempt to keep the Man of Tomorrow and the Caped Crusader relevant for younger audiences—considering that competitor Marvel Comics was making a splash on high school and college campuses—several issues of the long-running *World's Finest Comics* were handed over to the college-age offspring of the most famous superheroes in the world: the Super Sons of Batman and Superman.

Wearing costumes that were indistinguishable duplicates of their fathers' famous duds, the boy heroes went about their crime-fighting under the sound-alike pseudonyms of Superman Jr. and Batman Jr. Their civilian identities weren't any more creative: Clark Kent Jr. and Bruce Wayne Jr. Clark wore glasses identical to his father's everyday disguise, though in his defense, the son of Superman did bear just the merest hint of sideburns.

The Super Sons were intended to reflect the concerns of the college-age audience, and their adventures had them struggling to overcome the generation gap with their stodgy, often-disapproving dads. Beyond that, the Super Sons found occasion to cross swords with hinky self-help cults and suspicious gurus, not to mention out-of-control women's libbers—from space! The Super Sons didn't skimp on the teen slang of the day, either—or at least what the writers imagined that slang to be. Batman Jr. complains of a long trip's "endless highway jive." Superman Jr. laments his lack of "bread." They both refer to women as "chicks" and "dolls"—it's oh so very hip.

That the stories took place in the contemporary 1970s made for a puzzling situation. At the very least, it raised the question of how Superman and Batman were suddenly fathers to teenaged sons. In the elder heroes' individual titles, they remained unmarried and childless, but here Batman and Superman had wives (with their faces always hidden to keep readers guessing) and were no older than they were depicted in the pages of *Action Comics* or *Detective Comics*. Even Batman's sidekick Robin was still a teenager, yet apparently a peer to Batman!

In their final appearance, it was revealed that the Super Sons had only ever been computer simulations, created by Superman and Batman to judge whether fatherhood was a possibility, given the demands of their crime-fighting careers. Briefly brought to real life, the young heroes sacrificed themselves to save the world—although as figments of a computer program's imagination, there's always a possibility that the Super Sons could return someday.

THUNDERBUNNY

"I have great power, but I become a rabbit to use it? I don't know if being a superhero is worth it!"

THE LONG-LASTING APPEAL of superheroes can be attributed, at least in part, to their inherent escapism, especially for young readers. Kids can imagine themselves decked out in a colorful costume and possessing all those wonderful powers, gadgets, and skills. Some heroes, like the original Captain Marvel, capitalize on that sense of wonder by having the hero transform from a child into a superpowered champion.

Such a transformation happens to Bobby Caswell, adolescent comic book fan, when he stumbles across a crashed spaceship. The ship's sole denizen—the last survivor of a doomed civilization—passes on to Bobby the power of his planet's greatest hero. All Bobby must do is concentrate, clap his hands, and he is transformed—into a giant pink rabbit clad in Spandex!

It's an absurd turn of events, though not a completely raw deal. While inhabiting the form of Thunderbunny, Bobby gains tremendous strength, is invulnerable to harm, and can move and fly with the speed of lightning. The one drawback (aside from looking like Bugs Bunny on steroids): the longer he remains in Thunderbunny's impressive cartoon-headed form, the more difficult it is to return to his human self. Bobby Caswell runs the risk of becoming an anthropomorphic bunny *for life*!

Bobby's superheroic career straddled an impressive line between spoof and homage. Facing foes like Doctor Fog, Snaka (an evil snake sporting cybernetic arms), and the robotic Big C.A.M., he also found the opportunity to team up with fellow superheroes the Mighty Crusaders, the THUNDER Agents, and even an assortment of obscure Golden Age heroes like Pat Parker, War Nurse (page 55) and Magicman.

Thunderbunny was one rabbit who had trouble finding a permanent hutch. The character originally appeared in fanzines—small-run magazines printed, edited, and distributed by comic book fans—before landing at Charlton Comics. When that company sold its stock of superheroes to DC Comics, Thunderbunny suddenly became homeless. Red Circle, a superhero-friendly imprint of Archie Comics, provided an early home, as did Warp Graphics. Thunderbunny then hopped over to Apple Comics, where his luck finally ran out.

Thunderbunny hasn't popped up since then, but it's comforting to know that—as of his final appearance—Bobby hadn't yet been permanently trapped in the form of his lagomorphic alter ego.

Created by:
Martin Greim

Debuted in:
Charlton Bullseye #6
(Charlton Comics, March 1982)

Other career options:
Delivering Easter eggs; outsmarting hunters with speech impediments

© 1982 by Martin Greim

U.S. 1

"I was beginning to forget what being a trucker was all about ... "

Created by:
Al Milgrom and
Herb Trimpe

Debuted in:
U.S. 1 #1 (Marvel
Comics, May 1983)

His current 20:
Hammer down for
the Milky Way

©1983 by Marvel Comics

AH, THE CHALLENGING LIFE of the American trucker: long hours, endless miles, tight deadlines, alien spaceships powered by raw chicken, black-masked whip-wielding motorcycle villains, cybernetic skull implants that allow a driver to control his truck telepathically . . .

The intent of *U.S. 1* was to excite kids' imagination about a set of collectible toy trucks. When the toy line failed to materialize, however, *U.S. 1* developed a spectacular world of its own—a world centered on trucking. *U.S. 1* depicts Ulysses Solomon Archer, natural athlete and born genius. U.S. seems to have a bright future ahead of him, but all he wants to do is drive a rig like his brother Jefferson. Then the pair is driven off the road by the seemingly supernatural Highwayman, a truck driver who sends unsuspecting long-haul truckers to their doom.

Jeff is believed dead in the crash, but U.S. makes it out, albeit in postsurgical possession of a high-tech metal shell replacing most of his damaged skull. Discovering that his skullcap lets him tap into C.B. broadcasts, Archer turns his consider-able intellect toward outfitting his rig (the eponymous U.S. 1) with electronics more advanced than NASA mission control. His goal: find the Highwayman!

U.S. 1 exists in an entertainingly absurd world where long-haul trucking is the alpha and omega of existence. The battle for the highways even attracts the attention of an extraterrestrial race (who, of course, speak English by way of C.B. lingo: "Breaker breaker, good buddy!"). Every struggle seems to find its way back to the truck stop dive the Short Stop and its thematically nicknamed regulars (Wide Load Annie, Retread, Poppa Wheelie, and—straining the credulity of fanciful nicknaming—a wild-child lady trucker named Taryn "Down the Highway" O'Connell).

Archer faces Baron von Blimp and his Neo-Nazi soldiers; runs a deadly cross-country race hauling chicken parts at the behest of the checker-suited Chicken Colonel; and discovers his rig can be commanded telepathically, thanks to his C.B. skull. Then he confronts the Highwayman on the biggest stage of them all: outer space! As his alien pal "Al" explains: "What the universe really needs are truckers . . . men of courage and intelligence who are strong-willed and independent! Men who could stand up to the rigors, and most especially the solitude, of space!"

Freed from the limitations of earth-bound stories, Archer's rig is converted into a space-faring cargo vessel, the Short Stop is rebuilt as the space-based Star Stop, and U.S. Archer drives the great two-lane among the stars.